MYSTERY OF THE

PIPER'S GHOST

BY ZILLAH K. MACDONALD

Cover and illustrations by Charles Beck

SCHOLASTIC BOOK SERVICES

NEW YORK · LONDON · RICHMOND HILL, ONTARIO

To

HELEN and PAUL

in grateful thanks

6th printing . . . . December 1966

Printed in the U.S.A.

CONTENTS

1. A FIGHT AND WHAT CAME OF IT

"HI, MICHAEL! Lend a hand!" Michael sprang up to obey the call. He had been sitting with his back to the sea, watching something that was happening on the high rocky hill that circled the cove of Portopeake, in Nova Scotia. He had not heard Colin's boat "making in."

A rope snaked up and fell at his feet.

Michael snatched up the line and ran to a piling farther up the wharf. As he made it fast, he glanced down at the beach. The tide was on the turn. It fell fast. They would have to keep careful watch. The falling water would take the boat down with the tide. The line must be slanted. Otherwise, the boat might be hung up and the lines would snap, setting it adrift. He hurried to do the same for the stern line.

Colin shoved his lunch box over the edge of the dock. He was a bit awkward about it. He had injured his knee on a slippery deck and had been using a crutch.

"See anything of Lennie?" he cried. "Lennie promised to help me unload my traps."

"No, Colin! But I could help. I'm strong," Michael answered.

Colin smiled up at the eleven-year-old. "Fine, Michael!" he said. Colin was six feet tall and in college. Michael thought him one of the finest.

The older boy dropped back into the boat. With crutch to steady him, he began heaving up the traps. But first he removed the stone that weighted them. He flipped the smelly bait into the sea where a crowd of gulls swept down upon them, mewing greedily.

"They act as if they haven't had a meal in weeks," Michael said.

Colin laughed. "Maybe they've got short memories. Here, Michael. Catch!" Colin swung up an empty trap. Michael caught it, walked with it across the dock and laid it neatly against the edge of the far side.

He worked with a strength beyond his eleven years.

His body was thin and tall for his age. His face bony and white. A pair of startlingly blue eyes looked out from under a thatch of black hair. People seeing Michael for the first time thought he was frail. The children of Portopeake were red-cheeked, summer and winter, and more stockily built. There were German and Irish strains in this country. But Michael was not frail. He was wiry and strong, typical of that part of the Scotch Highlands which his name suggested. He could have been a Cape Bretoner, that island at Nova Scotia's eastern end. But he wasn't. Oddly, he was an American, left with Ma Lovey when only a few months old.

As he waited for the traps to come up over the edge of the wharf, Michael looked again toward the jagged rocks that rose above the cove. That bright spot of color, high up by the trail to the old mine shaft, was Margot, and those two other figures, outlined against the September sky, belonged to Allwyn and Stephen. His gang had gone up there for a picnic supper. They had not asked him to go with them. They were punishing him for the fight he had had with Allwyn yesterday. Well, who cared? But he did care. He was hurt that they had gone off without him.

He wished he had not started the fight. He could still hear Mary Ellen's shocked voice. She had come to the party to help Ma Lovey with the games and the supper. She belonged in Colin's crowd.

"Oh, Michael!" she had cried. "Fighting at your own birthday party. A great boy like you, eleven years old today."

Michael was very much ashamed about the fight. But when a fellow said things about your parents, mean things, you had to fight him. He'd fight Allwyn again, if Allwyn said the same things.

Anyway, he told himself, working for Colin, one of the big boys, was more fun. Girls were no good to play with. They always wanted to boss you. He went on stacking the traps into a neat wall.

Several of them were neatly piled on the side of the dock when Michael heard a voice whistling "Hail! Hail! The Gang's All Here!" Lennie was coming!

A tall, thickset boy, with the beginning of a stoop, rounded the fishhouse. His hair was red like Allwyn's. All the Moorhans were redheads. Lennie was two years younger than Colin and still in school. He was always whistling, or singing, when he was not playing the small portable radio that he carried with him everywhere he went.

Lennie spied Michael and glared at him.

"Look!" he said. "You beat up my brother yesterday!"

Michael shivered inside and braced himself for what was coming. Ma Lovey had warned him there might be trouble.

"I gave it to him good," he said boldly. Michael was no coward.

Lennie's face cleared. "O.K.," he said. "Serves him right, the sprat."

Michael was startled. He had never had brothers or sisters. But if he had had them, he did not think he would be talking of them as Lennie was.

"Oh, come now, Len!" Colin's voice rose over the wharf edge. "Allwyn is your own brother."

"Well, what of it? I'd have given it to him myself, long ago, only Father won't let me touch him. He—he talks too much."

Michael was surprised. Lennie thought of Allwyn much as he did himself. It seemed to make them pals. And that was odd, he thought, because he had never really liked Lennie.

Lennie leaned over the side of the dock. "Sorry, Colin!" he called down. "I got kept. Father wanted me to tie up some toggles." Toggles were the glass floats, usually ginger beer bottles, tied to the lobster lines between the trap on the bottom and the buoy on the surface. Nova Scotia tides were high and the lines had to be slack. The toggles kept the lines off the bottom.

Lennie regarded the neatly stacked traps. "Some job!" he commented. "A good job, too."

Michael stood up proudly. Praise from the big boys was something.

Lennie placed the radio he was carrying on the dock edge. He stopped whistling and turned it on. An army band playing a rousing march filled the air. Lennie dropped down to the boat and took over Colin's job.

Michael found himself swinging up the traps and crossing the dock in time to the march. He had a wonderful feeling. The melody lingered in his head long after the march stopped and was replaced by a voice talking. Lennie switched off the radio. He liked only music.

The last trap came up. Colin swung himself to the

dock after it. He began untying the bowline, giving it more slack. Lennie did the same with the stern one. The boat was moving up the wharf on the falling tide, as the slanted lines became perpendicular.

Michael looked up the hill. He hoped Margot and Stephen and Allwyn were watching him with the big boys.

Lennie and Colin started up the path to the main road which touched the head of the cove. They had just reached it when a car shot past at breakneck speed. None of them had seen it before. The soft gravel shoulders of the road rose up in a cloud of dirt and hit them like bullets.

"Hey!" Lennie cried angrily after it. "Where do you think you're going?"

"It's the strangers!" Colin was angry, too.

"Yah!" Lennie answered. "They've come to open up the old mine. They were talking to Father about it."

Michael thought excitedly, this is news to tell Ma Lovey!

"But Lennie," Colin cried, "the mine's worked out. Everyone knows that."

"The strangers say differently," Lennie announced. He cocked his red head on one side. "What do you know? Whenever the Piper walks out of the Pool, something happens in Portopeake. They say he's walking again, and —the mine is to open."

"Oh, Lennie!" Colin turned on him impatiently. "You're not going to raise that old ghost, are you?"

"Well," and Lennie sounded mysterious, "there are

those who have seen the weird sight. I'm thinking of walking out there tonight to see for myself."

Then Michael, feeling one of them, spoke up. "That ghost is a crazy story!" Ma Lovey had always impressed on him the foolishness of the local legend. Her code with him had been, don't be afraid of anything but an untruth. For some reason, the younger generation had a wholesome fear of the Piper.

"So there aren't any ghosts!" Lennie turned on him. "Just for that, big mouth, you'll go with me tonight!" And Michael thought, Lennie is just as nasty as Allwyn. He's quick-tongued, too.

"Oh, lay off, Lennie," Colin broke in. "Michael is just a kid."

"I'm not either," Michael cried hotly. "I'll go with you, Lennie. I'm not afraid!"

"O.K.," Lennie agreed. "You meet me on the high ridge by ten-thirty. The Piper walks at midnight—when he walks."

"Lennie, shut up, can't you?" Colin sounded impatient. "Don't you go unless you want to go, Michael. And thanks for the help. 'By."

Colin went off to his home high on the ridge near the church. Lennie turned to the right.

Michael continued along the road on the left. The farther he walked, the more doubtful he became concerning the night's trip. He had visited the Piper's Pool once before. And he could still remember the bearded trees and the feeling of uneasiness they had given him. He didn't like to think of them after dark.

He wondered, too, what Ma Lovey would think of the midnight adventure. Maybe he'd better not mention it to her. She might say he could not go. But he had to go now. He had given his word to Lennie that he would go. But he wished he could tell Ma Lovey about the trip. He had always told her everything.

Ma Lovey, although she had brought him up, was not his mother. But he knew she had lavished on him a mother's care ever since he could remember.

Eleven years before, while the villagers were in church attending a Christmas Eve candlelight service, a small private plane with engines skipping, clearly in trouble, had cruised over the church. The minister had rushed out with his flock and endeavored to line up a runway with candles and lanterns. But the plane had crashed on the glacier rocks. Of the four persons in the plane, only one lived. A small bundle wrapped in blankets had been thrown clear. Ma Lovey had taken the baby home. And she had found in his blankets a hastily scrawled note, apparently written at the last moment, "His name is Michael Alistair Cunningham, Scotch-American, September 10—" the writing trailed off. Later inquiry proved the couple's name had not been Cunningham. And odder still no inquiries for a lost baby had been received. It happened in wartime when families were widely scattered. Ma Lovey was glad to keep him.

When Michael grew old enough to question, Ma Lovey told him the truth. She made a great point of the fact that he had arrived on Christmas, the most wonderful present she had ever had. She tried to make him see that

8

the couple in the plane had used their last frantic moments to establish his name, nationality and birthday. And that could only mean that he had an honored name and must live up to it. He must be truthful and generous and brave in all he did.

Every child in school was familiar with Michael's story. The time was bound to come when someone would refer to his lack of parents.

So at the party Allwyn had cried, half in pique for a fancied injury, "They didn't want you, Michael. They were glad to get rid of you." But Michael didn't think the remark funny. Suddenly he seemed to hear the whole village repeating it. The words cut like a whip. He lashed out at Allwyn.

Michael recalled the fight as he trudged home. He had been frightened when Allwyn hit back with a strength which almost bowled him over. But he could still recall the strange sense of power that had welled up in him while he was fighting. He had enjoyed the fight. That was what frightened him now. Shame had come only later.

Michael considered the hill. Wild blueberries and brambles, sumac and elderberry and rangy spruce hid the rocks in summer. But here and there the boulders were showing. Fall was approaching. Later the winter would thrash the hill with wild Atlantic winds, drenching rainstorms, and white blizzards.

He thought of the night's adventure. If he didn't go, Lennie would say he was "kid stuff" and refuse to be friends. He might even call him "yellow." Besides, the thought of seeing a ghost was a bit exciting. He hoped Ma would not learn of the trip and stop him.

"Michael!" Ma's voice reached him as he opened the kitchen door.

Ma herself was just coming through the doorway from the front room. She was a small woman, slight as a young girl, with naturally curly blond hair, cut short, and eyes of forget-me-not blue that could be piercing. She had on a white uniform and carried her nurse's satchel.

Ma was a graduate nurse. She had given up her work to take care of Michael. Lately she had gone back to her profession again. The village said it was to earn money for Michael. Clothes and food for a growing boy took money. His parents had evidently felt no responsibility for him. Ma never discussed the matter.

"Michael," Ma Lovey said, "old Granny Westerley has been taken bad, and they sent for me. I've never left you alone at night before. But you're a big boy now. Of course, there is nothing to fear here in Portopeake."

Michael's first thought was, now he could get away. "I won't be afraid, Ma," he assured her. She looked relieved.

"You didn't go to the picnic with the others?" She sounded surprised.

Michael squirmed. "I—I was helping Colin with his traps," he said.

Ma's glance was sharp. She said, "I'm glad you were able to help Colin, Michael. He's a fine lad. But I don't want you to get into the habit of hanging around with Lennie and the older boys. You're too young."

10

"Yes, Ma," he answered a bit guiltily and hurriedly added, "I've got news, Ma! The strangers have come to open the mines."

Ma shook her head. "They won't stay long." Her tone was confident. "Kejimakujee is worked out."

A car honked at the foot of the hill.

Ma patted his shoulder. "Good-by, Michael," she said. "Supper is ready for you. If Granny should go during the night, I might get back before morning." She dropped a quick kiss on his cheek and rushed away.

Michael ate his supper and washed the dishes. The house seemed very empty without Ma Lovey. He decided he would not go to bed. Instead, he set the alarm and dozed off in the big chair.

Four hours later the peal awakened him. For a moment he didn't understand where he was. Then he remembered Lennie and the trip.

When he opened the back door, the whole hill was silver and gray with a spangled arc of velvety blue overhead. The climb to the ridge was sharp, and he paused, panting, halfway. The cove below was a black pool of polished glass. The white hulls of the boats made them look like ghost ships.

A car sped by on the road below. He recognized Joe Westerley's jeep. Had Granny Westerly already started the long journey? Would Ma be back? And what would she think of his absence?

A shrill whistle cut the night. He answered. Lennie rose out of the shadows.

"It's a night!" Lennie greeted him. "Thought maybe

you'd got scared and weren't coming." The tone annoyed Michael.

"I came all right," he answered shortly.

"O.K.," Lennie said. "Let's get going."

2.   IS IT A GHOST?

IN SILENCE they kept the pace. Just before leaving the high rocks, Lennie stopped and swung around. "Hey!" he cried.

"What's the matter?" Michael demanded. Then he saw what had startled Lennie. The left arm of the cove was known as Slim Point. There were two old houses out there, which had once been used as summer cottages, but they had not been lived in for several years. "The old house is all lit up!" Michael cried.

"Must be the strangers," Lennie decided. "Father said they were inquiring about the house on the point. Must like their own company to go 'way out there. Come on, let's get going!"

Lennie started across the ridge, Michael following. If the strangers had taken a house, they must mean business, Michael thought.

Lennie led the way through the ghostly silence of the dead forest. Now and then he stooped to dodge a low, mossy branch; Michael, following close behind, felt the branch trailing down his spine like ghostly fingers. He was beginning to think they must be almost there when Lennie left the path beside a bramble patch and dived in under the trees. Excitement quivered through Michael. Lennie signaled for silence and flung himself flat on his face, wriggling his body forward under the low branches of some spruce.

Michael, fearful of losing him, crowded closer.

"Here we are," Lennie whispered at last.

Michael understood better why Lennie had left the path. On the other side of the trees the land ended abruptly. They were on top of a scarp. In front of them the rock sheered away, as sharply as if cut with a knife. They were looking straight down into the spruce-ringed basin which held the Piper's Pool. Curiosity filled Michael.

He recalled that they said the Pool never froze on the coldest night. They also said it was bottomless, fed from an inner spring in the rock.

Michael had heard Lennie's father say it did not freeze because of its warm walls of spruce. But he had also been present when Elmira McCabe, the postmistress, had said, "It's the evil one that lives in its depths, keeps it warm." The stories were all a part of the mystery of the place.

The water of the Pool seemed very still. It shone like a dark mirror. Silence was all around them. Nonetheless, Michael had a feeling as if something were moving nearby.

It was damp under the spruce, but the air was warm.

14

They were both watching tensely. How long they waited, he couldn't tell. It might have been hours, he thought. Then, at last, something happened. The still surface of the Pool began to ripple.

"Hist!" Lennie's voice was excited.

The sound Michael had felt himself waiting for came. A moaning cry rose and fell shrilly. Its mournfulness chilled him. He wanted to stop up his ears and forget it. But the cry continued, ending abruptly on a plaintive note. He had a feeling that fear and pain were mingled in the cry, and something else he couldn't understand. What had made the sound? Was something terribly hurt down there?

Lennie's hand was clutching his shoulder. The ripples on the water were increasing. They continued to watch. Something was disturbing the Pool from within. What would they see? Then—the surface of the water was pierced by a strange object. Something that glittered in the moonlight. It suggested a head—a head with horns! Something was rising out of the Pool and moving toward the bank!

"The Piper!" breathed Lennie. His voice was full of awe.

Michael never took his eyes from the strange object. He saw it was a head, because a body with two legs followed it. It *was* the Piper! Those shaftlike objects over his shoulder must be the pipes. Under one arm he carried a bulky sack, the bag of the pipes.

Within a foot of the shore the figure paused. It raised one foot, stork-fashion. Then Michael and Lennie froze

15

with horror. The foot was webbed! And over the whole figure was a satiny sheen, an unearthly glow.

It was leaving the Pool now. Michael, in his hiding place, cowered lower. He had a feeling that the awful thing might waft itself up to him, like ocean spray.

The figure paused on a jutting rock. It lifted the other foot. Then it suddenly moved toward the spruce trees and was swallowed into the shadows. There were only the widening ripples on the Pool to show that something had been there.

Some tension in Lennie broke. He jumped up.

"There's something I've got to see," he cried. Circling a little through the trees behind them, he found a ledge of rock sloping down to the rocks around the Pool. Lennie started slithering down. Michael scrambled after him, little shivers running up and down his spine.

Lennie picked a way across the open space to the rocks where the phantom had crossed on its way to the wood and stood there frowning.

Michael, too, stared down at the rocks. It was unbelievable. The Piper had risen out of the waters of the Pool. He had crossed the bare rocks and he had left *no footprints*. It was as if he hadn't been!

"Well!" Lennie exploded. "I suppose now, Michael, you'll still say there are no ghosts."

"No—o," Michael said doubtfully. "I—I guess I saw one."

"Good!" Lennie said. "You stick to that tomorrow." He turned and scrambled back up the cliff.

All the way down to the glacier rocks Michael kept

glancing uneasily over his shoulder. He had a feeling the bearded trees might produce the Piper at any moment.

He was troubled also by something else. All his life, so far, he had believed everything Ma had told him. But Ma had said there were no such things as ghosts, and he had seen one.

When they came at last to the high rocks, and the village lay below them, Lennie said, "Well, 'night now! You're some kid, Michael."

Michael was filled with pride.

When he got home, Ma wasn't back yet. He climbed thankfully into bed and immediately fell asleep.

Next morning he dressed quickly and went downstairs.

Ma was in the kitchen. For a minute she didn't notice him. She was sitting at the table warming her hands around a cup of tea. He had a frightened feeling she had forgotten all about him.

Then she looked up. Her face was white, her voice dull. "Granny's gone, Michael. We had a hard night. You'll have to eat your breakfast alone. I'm all in."

Ma got up and moved heavily toward the door. She seemed like someone different. Usually she darted about with the quickness of a hummingbird.

He ate hurriedly, then went upstairs for his hat and coat. Ma's door was open. She was lying on the bed, already fast asleep. He tiptoed in and threw an afghan over her. She never moved.

At the front door, downstairs, he paused. Late September mornings in Nova Scotia were sometimes chilly. He had begun to wear the muffler of Cunningham tartan which Ma had ordered for him from Scotland. She always tied it for him, giving him a little motherly pat as she finished. He missed the warmth of her presence.

In school Michael found it difficult to keep his mind on his lessons. He kept thinking of the Piper and how Ma had said there were no ghosts. He wanted so much to believe her.

Margot called to him to play with them at recess. He knew then he was forgiven for the fight. He wished he could forget Allwyn's words as easily. But the big piece of sticking plaster on Allywyn's forehead was a continual reminder. He was glad when Lennie called him.

He ran in answer and became instantly the center of a group of older boys.

"You saw the ghost, Michael, didn't you?" Lennie questioned him. Many of the older boys were sitting on a bit of rocky ledge which made a natural bleacher. They all seemed waiting for his answer.

"Yes, I did," Michael answered, adding, "but Ma Lovey says there are no ghosts."

"You forget about Ma Lovey." Lennie sounded angry. "You saw him come up out of the water as if he lived and breathed under it, didn't you? You saw him walk over the dry rock with wet feet and never leave any footprints. Isn't that so, Michael?"

"Yes, Lennie!"

"Hot-spot!" Llewellyn exploded. The boys looked at Michael admiringly. He felt important for the rest of the morning.

Later as he hurried home after school, cutting across the ridge, and slipping and sliding down to Ma Lovey's back door, his mind veered again to Allwyn's speech. He couldn't wait to talk to Ma.

He found her in the living room, looking down on the cove.

"Ma!" he demanded.

"What is it, Michael?"

He found it hard to begin. "Ma, do you think my father and mother put me on that plane because—because they wanted to get rid of me?"

"Why, Michael!" Ma's arm went around him. She drew him down beside her on the window seat. "Michael, who's been saying things like that?

"Michael," she said. "You must believe me. I examined everything you had on that morning very carefully. Nothing had been bought. Everything you had on had been hand-knitted or hand-sewn. And the person who did it hadn't been terribly experienced. You know, Michael, only a woman who wants her baby very much ever does that."

He felt better. What Allwyn said couldn't be true.

They were interrupted by a visitor.

Joe Westerley, Margot's uncle, and Granny's son, had come to bring them a fish. Ma accepted it from him gratefully.

"What's this I hear about the mine reopening, Joe?" she said.

The words seemed to excite Joe. "Portopeake is going places, Ma Lovey, when that mine opens."

"But I've always understood, Joe, that the mine was worked out."

Joe moved his head excitedly from side to side. "I know, Ma, but we were all mistaken. Mr. Budd and Mr. Harte—those are the strangers' names—say they've discovered a new lode in the mine. We're all going to be rich."

Ma looked up wistfully. "I'd like to make some money," she said. Michael wondered if he imagined seeing her eyes turn to his worn shoes. For the first time he realized that Ma Lovey must have spent a lot of money just keeping him in clothes.

"You put your savings in the mine, Ma," Joe urged. "They'll turn into gold."

After Joe left, Ma said, "Pa Lovey was an engineer, Michael. He said that mine was worked out. He wasn't one to make a mistake, ever." Ma sounded troubled.

3. PLANS TO OPEN THE MINE

MICHAEL, like the rest of the village, was all agog about the mine. When he went on an errand to the store for Ma, he often met the strangers. They were always talking loudly of the hidden gold still in Kejimakujee.

The one who did most of the talking was known as Ebenezer Budd. The other was Jonathan Harte. Beside the lean, wind-bitten faces of the Nova Scotian fishermen, Michael thought they both looked well fed and "soft."

Ebenezer wore an enormous plaid Mackinaw which he kept buttoned high about his throat. He complained loudly of the fog and the dampness. Now and then he whipped out a very fine, very white handkerchief and loudly blew his nose. He seemed to have a continual cold. At such times a large diamond on the little finger of his right hand winked brilliantly. The diamond fascinated Michael. He had not known a stone could have such life. Both men had a highhanded way of doing business which half the village resented and half admired.

More and more, Michael spent the school recess watching the older boys play ball. Once when a ball went wild and the boys on the rock jumped to their feet to try to catch it, Michael was the one who plucked it out of the air.

"Good work!" Lennie cried, and John and Llewellyn applauded. Michael felt important. After that he had a job.

They took to calling him "Snapper." When a ball went wild, they would all shout, "Hi, Snapper!" And Michael would tear off after the lost ball.

He didn't like the name very much. Snappers were lobsters so short that it was against the law to keep them. They had to be put back into the sea. Still, the nickname seemed to make him one of them.

Once Robert snickered, "That child is a sucker for work." He pretended he didn't hear. But he knew it was true. He liked work. He was happier working for Colin, or catching balls for the team, than he was playing tag with Margot and the younger boys and girls.

Margot, miffed that he no longer shared their games, followed him one day to the rock. Allwyn and Stephen and Velma trailed behind her. Willy watched them from the school steps.

Llewellyn, captain of the team, wasn't long in discovering they were there. Standing in front of them, feet wide apart, he scowled down at them.

"Look!" he shouted. "You kids are liable to get hurt. Scram! Michael can stay. He can take care of himself." Michael felt suddenly grown-up.

Margot and the others, with dark backward glances at Michael, left. And Michael thought, Allwyn hates me. He didn't like being beaten in the fight, and he's jealous because Lennie likes me. Stephen's glance had been wistful. Michael was sorry. He liked Stephen.

But the thing that really drew Michael to the older boys was Lennie's radio. There was a generous streak in the older boy. He kept the tiny thing in batteries and he let anyone play the radio who was willing to listen to a musical program. Michael loved music. Songs and marches made him happy. And these days, when Ma was off nursing, sometimes far into the evening or all night, he was very lonely.

"Ma, why don't we have a radio?" he asked one day.

Ma looked worried. Then she said lightly, "Maybe we

will someday, Michael." And she went on talking of something else.

He tried to talk to her about the ghost. The matter bothered him. Her answers were impatient. "Michael, surely you don't believe that story that Lennie Moorhans is spreading abroad. Even you are old enough to know it is childish. There are no ghosts!"

Michael, for once, was resentful. He had seen the ghost and it had certainly seemed real. Ma hadn't seen it. How could she know anything about the matter? She just had a "down" on Lennie. Suddenly her opinion of his friend seemed very unfair.

His troubled spirits showed in his actions at home. He was restless and moody.

"Michael Cunningham!" Ma cried one night, and her voice, usually so gentle, had an edge. She had been on her feet for twelve hours and was desperately tired. "Michael Cunningham! What is the matter with you? You're not the same boy at all lately. It's that older crowd. I hear you've been playing with them at recess. In the future, Michael, I don't want you hanging around Lennie and Llewellyn and that older gang. You're a little boy yet, Michael, even if you are eleven. They'll only get you into trouble."

He wasn't little and it was Ma who was different, he told himself resentfully. What was a fellow to do? Lennie liked him. He didn't think him a kid. And his own crowd didn't want him any more. He felt hurt although he really didn't want to be with Margot and the rest. He *had been* their leader.

But his love for Ma was great and, in the matter of the ghost, he tried to believe she was right. Maybe there was some explanation of its ability to come up out of the water. He made up his mind he would go out in daylight and see.

Saturday dawned cold and foggy, but Ma was away and Michael decided to make the trip. The thought of going out there alone frightened him. The bearded trees on a foggy day were much more eerie. But he remembered Ma had said that he must be brave because he had an honored name.

The walk out and back to the Piper's Pool would take at least two hours. He made himself an egg sandwich to take with him.

Up and up and up, over the high rocks, then across the ridge, and at last into the forest. The bearded trees, when he came to them, loomed ghostlike out of the fog. He almost turned back. But he kept on. He had a moment of uncertainty finding the bramble patch where Lennie had turned off. Then he wriggled in under the trees and came out on the bluff. The fog was still high overhead; the Pool was clear. Looking down into it, he saw a curious sight. The sides of the Pool were in ledges like steps.

Then sweat broke out all over him. He had a sense of something near him, as he had had before with Lennie. Only now he was alone. Frantically he crawled back to the bramble trail. Had the Piper been lurking in the bushes above the Pool?

He was straightening up when he caught a quick breath behind him. He swung around as a frightened voice cried, "Michael, I—I thought you were a ghost!"

Michael felt a little foolish when he found himself facing a friend—Willy, Auntie Sammy's adopted son. She worked for most of the villagers and lived farther along the ridge, beyond the hermit's cabin.

"Michael, you scared me almost to death," Willy admitted. He looked as frightened as Michael.

"Hello, Willy!" Michael greeted him. "What are you doing 'way out here alone?" Willy had a pail but it was too late for berries and too early for nuts.

"I come here sometimes, Michael," Willy said. "Auntie Sammy says the water of the Pool is witched. She thinks it cures the annoyance in her legs." Willy came close to him and Michael thought, Willy is glad to see me. He's frightened, too. They started back together.

"Did you ever see the Piper, Willy?"

Willy began to look around uneasily. He lowered his voice. "Only once, Michael. It was awful late at night. Auntie Sammy was taken bad. She cried out I was to get her some water from the Piper's Pool."

"You came out here, alone—at *midnight*, Willy!" Michael was filled with admiration for his courage.

"I was awful scared, Michael," Willy admitted.

"You think the Piper is a ghost?"

Willy nodded his head. "Yes, of course he's a ghost, Michael. He came right up out of the water and stood on the edge of the rock like a heron, one foot in the air. He was all shiny and funny-looking. Then he walked away." Michael knew then that Willy had seen what he had seen himself. And Willy had been alone.

Once back on the ridge, Michael dropped on the rocks and pulled out his sandwich. He carefully divided it and handed Willy half. Willy's eyes grew large with wonder and with something else. Michael had a dreadful feeling that Willy was thin because he was hungry.

"You want to see something, Michael?" Willy said as he gathered up the last crumb.

Michael nodded.

Willy led him a short distance and pointed over under the trees.

On an old wood trail back of the stand of spruce Michael could see an expensive new car. The car was the shiny new one that had sped past Lennie and Colin and himself.

"They went up to Kejimakujee, Michael," Willy said. "They went right up and into the shaft house. Ever been up to the gold mine, Michael?"

Michael hadn't.

"I'll show you," Willy offered and led the way up the side trail. A gold mine sounded like the Arabian Nights to Michael. But when they came in sight of the entrance at last, he was badly disappointed.

"It's only a shanty," he cried.

The two-story building was leaning out of line at every corner, its second floor drunkenly askew, its chimney tottering.

"I guess it will make a big noise," Willy said, "when it falls down."

The door was open and they gazed inside.

As his eyes grew used to the gloom, Michael saw that

the place was littered with oddments. There was a wide sloping shelf that had evidently been used as a desk. Here and there a torn, faded blueprint still clung to the moldering walls. The four small windows were murky with cobwebs. A ladderlike stairway led to the upper story. But what held Michael's attention was a huge, square, black spot on the far side of the floor. He stepped over the threshold and walked toward it.

"Michael, watch out!" Willy's warning stopped him. He jerked back. The black spot was a hole, like an enormous well. Then he noticed a fragile-looking ladder attached to one side of the hole, leading down. This was the shaft of the mine.

"They went down the ladder," Willy whispered excitedly. "I saw them. One was kind of scared. I wouldn't go down there for anything. There are ghosts down there."

"Don't be silly," Michael said stoutly. He didn't feel afraid like Willy. He wanted to go down the ladder. He wondered if the gold hung in clumps from the walls. Then he remembered. Ma said the mine was worked out. That meant the gold was gone.

At that moment the shaft ladder began to quiver. "They're coming up," Willy cried. "They'll find us. Come away, Michael." He fled.

But Michael stayed. The shaking ladder fascinated him. A man's hand appeared, and he caught the flash of a diamond ring and knew its owner must be Mr. Budd. The hand reached for the top rung. Then a head and shoulders followed. Cautiously the figure pulled itself over the edge.

Mr. Budd stepped off the ladder as his companion appeared.

"The Piper's our chance," Mr. Budd cried, his eyes on his companion below him. "Everything will be all right."

"Lucky he started walking again." Mr. Harte laughed as if it were a great joke. "It shouldn't be hard to fix that shabby hermit, Zeb."

Then they turned. They saw Michael standing in the shadows beside the doorway.

"Watch it!" Mr. Harte warned. And in a voice that sounded furiously angry, Mr. Budd, looking up, cried, "Who are *you*? How long have you been here?"

"I just came," Michael answered. He did not like the tone of the voice, but it was too dim to see their faces clearly.

"Well, you listen to me," Mr. Budd cried. "You get out of here and stay out. Do you hear what I say? Don't come back, ever."

"No, sir," Michael answered. He turned and walked away. He walked slowly. They needn't think he was afraid of them. Their voices followed him.

"Who's the kid?" Mr. Harte demanded. "He looks different."

"He is," Mr. Budd replied. "He's an American. Someone dumped him on Ma Lovey years ago. Probably not too bright. He doesn't count."

Willy was waiting for Michael down the trail. Michael felt warmed by his admiring glance. Willy thought he had been brave to stay and face the strangers. His admiration took some of the hurt out of the strangers' remarks.

Willy was funny, he thought, so brave over big things like going to the Pool at midnight, and so frightened of speaking to two strangers.

"Did they say anything?" Willy demanded.

"Nothing much," Michael answered. He was glad Willy hadn't heard their words. Why had they called him an "American" in that scornful tone of voice? And why was he different? He didn't feel any different from Colin, who was Scotch, too. His father was the minister. And why had they said he didn't count?

"Think they'll find gold in the mine, Michael?" Willy asked.

"I don't know, Willy."

Willy sighed. "I'd like to be rich. I'd fill all Auntie Sammy's potato sacks with gold."

Michael walked slowly over the glacier rocks to the trail he had made down to Ma Lovey's back door.

"Probably not too bright," the strangers had said. The words stung. He was as bright as anyone in school. The teacher had often said so. And the strangers had made the word "American" sound like something not nice.

4. LENNIE'S LOBSTER ROAST

MICHAEL knew that Indian summer was still ahead with its warm, balmy days. But the strong Atlantic breeze stirring the thinning foliage of the hill made him feel as if winter were close at hand. The air was crisp and even biting in the shadows. He pulled the tartan muffler more closely about his throat.

Michael was climbing the high rocks in search of Willy. He could usually be found looking for birds' nests, or watching some small wild thing fighting for its living in the crevices of the rocks. Aunt Sammy said, "Willy's my boy, and he's not going to get into trouble. Playing on the ridge never hurt anyone, or anything."

He didn't find Willy. But he did meet the Mountie and Scout. The officer's scarlet coat showed like holly berries against the rusting foliage. His face under his wide-brimmed hat, although stern-featured, was kindly. His golden-brown collie, Scout, pattered up to Michael and lifted a paw to be shaken.

"Hello!" Captain MacKay greeted him.

"I guess Scout likes me," Michael said. The dog's friendship always gave him a warm feeling inside.

"He certainly does, Michael," the captain agreed. Then he added quietly, "You better be a good boy, Michael.

31

Scout is very choosy about his friends." Man and dog walked on.

Michael wondered why the Mountie had spoken as he did. Had he heard of the midnight adventure to the Piper's Pool with Lennie?

A jingle of bells caught his ear, and he realized that the Moorhans' oxen were plodding up Church Hill, a low platform swung between four wheels behind them. Lennie was driving. With him were three of the older boys, Robert and Llewellyn and John.

Lennie saw him and waved the long whip he was using.

"Hi, Michael! We're off for a load of winter wood. Want to come along?"

Michael hesitated, remembering what Ma had said about hanging around with the older boys. But this wasn't hanging around with them. This was work, he argued. He thought resentfully of the long, lonely day ahead. Then one of the oxen jerked its head, and the bells sent their sweet tinkling notes into the crisp air.

The sound was so gay. He had to hear it again. Michael stepped aboard, but he was a little uneasy about what he was doing.

The oxen plodded up and over the ridge and down the hill on the other side. It was the road that Michael had taken before, in going to the Piper's Pool. But instead of turning off, halfway, now they kept going down. He could see the village of Cameronia there to the right. That patch of black against the rusty background was Father Stephen in his cassock. He was hurrying into his church. The priest interested Michael. None of his flock lived in

Portopeake, but he was a friend of Mr. Glendinning's and sometimes visited him. He had a smile and a greeting for all he met.

Michael had never been so far over the ridge before. He was excited and glad he had come.

Presently they entered a trail on the left, far below the Piper's Pool. They followed it until it ended at sea level in a dark cove.

With a loud cry, Lennie stopped the oxen in the wooded clearing. The gay jingle of bells ceased.

"Get out, Snapper!" Lennie ordered. Michael jumped off eagerly. The boys threw him their packages of lunch to catch.

"Get some chips and start a fire going," Lennie ordered. "We'll load the wood while you're doing it." The bells jingled again. The oxen plodded off.

The cut wood was stacked with its ends toward him in a golden wall all around the clearing. The air had a Christmasy tang of fresh balsam boughs.

Michael got busy. He could hear the boys' voices nearby mingled with the hollow tinkle of the oxen's bells. Building a fire, even by himself, was fun. There were plenty of chips from the cuttings nearby.

The evergreens made a warm wall on three sides of the clearing. On the fourth was the still, salty water of the cove, green in the shadows along the shore and dotted here and there with orange and white lobster buoys. The tide was high and the cove was full.

When the fire was going briskly, he picked up the lunch baskets and began to unpack them. Then he discovered

33

that Lennie had brought his radio, wrapped up in an old sweater in a biscuit box. He tuned in to CHNS and found it relaying a program of the B.B.C. "Maxwelton's braes are bonnie!" drifted out on the crisp air. Michael thought, The firs are bending nearer to listen.

The fire was so hot he slipped off his coat and muffler and laid them on a nearby log.

When the truck was loaded, the boys came running back.

"Some fire, Snapper!" Llewellyn cried, and Michael was proud and happy. They stood warming their hands at the fire, their eyes gazing into the cove.

"Hey!" Lennie cried. "How about a lobster roast? I think I'll visit my traps."

Robert grinned, and Llewellyn said, "Do, Lennie."

Michael, eager to be one of them, demanded, "Let me go with you, Lennie. I'm good at lifting traps."

"Fine, Michael!" Lennie agreed. They all went down to the cove. Lennie walked straight to a clump of spruce, as if he had gone there often before. He pushed out a leaky dory. They dumped out the rain water, and Lennie and Michael got in. The traps were close inshore. The others stood on shore and watched.

The first trap Lennie lifted was empty, and a shout went up from the shore. But in the second and third traps, they pulled up a couple of counters; that was a name given to lobsters of legal size for catching. After lifting ten traps, they had six counters and two snappers. Michael picked up the snappers to throw them back into the water.

"Hey!" Lennie shouted. "What are you up to?"

"I'm putting them back, Lennie. It's the law."

"What's the law got to do with us out here?" Lennie growled and snatched them from him.

As they climbed the path back to the fire, Michael said, "Lennie, those buoys were orange and white. Your colors are blue and green."

Lennie pretended surprise. "Now what do you know about that?" The others laughed, and Lennie seemed to regain his good humor.

"Won't Cy be surprised when he comes all the way out here tonight, and finds—ten empty traps? Say, fellows, aren't we having fun?"

Michael didn't like what they had done. Cy was a DP who had recently come to Portopeake. His name being unpronounceable, Cy Sullivan was as close as they got to it. He worked hard for others and had just begun to set a few traps for himself. He rarely spoke to anyone. But sometimes on quiet evenings he went up to the high rocks, and the clear notes of a bugle fell on the evening air. Michael loved to listen. Cy was supposed to have been in a band. Michael hated to think of Cy losing his catch, but he had to admit that the lobsters, roasted in their shells over the hot seaweed, tasted very good. They made a game of throwing their shells into the fire. Some, missing their mark, scattered around.

When it was time to go, Lennie cautioned Michael sternly. "Now see here, Snapper, don't you go spilling this to Ma Lovey. She'll tell the Mountie and first thing you know, we'll all be in the drink."

Robert scowled. "Why did you bring him, Lennie, if you're afraid he'll tell?"

"I like him along," Lennie said. "Snapper, kick out the fire."

All the way back, perched on the fresh-smelling spruce and birchwood, the boys joked about "Lennie's lobsters." Michael wondered what Cy would do when he discovered his loss. He had a feeling Cy would be nasty if once aroused. But, of course, he'd never find out who did it.

Then he found the boys were talking about Colin. John was saying, "Colin wants some spruce bows for his lobster traps. I told him the best were in the stand near Zeb's cabin."

"Try to get them with Zeb there," Llewellyn said.

"Those trees don't belong to Zeb," Robert cried. "Anyone can have them."

"Maybe," Llewellyn answered. "But Zeb won't allow anyone to go near them. He has a mean tongue and he keeps a wild dog."

"Oh, Zeb's dog isn't so bad," Lennie said.

"Ever see him?" Llewellyn demanded. "And—hear him?"

"Tangled with him," Lennie said lightly. They stared at him. "I laid that dog out good."

"Hot-spot!" Robert exploded. "I never saw him but I heard him once. I wouldn't attack that demon even with a gun."

"Leave it to your uncle Lennie." Lennie sat back and accepted their admiration like a hero.

But Michael was no longer paying attention. Colin had

always been good to him. Colin needed bows for his traps and because of his accident was unable to get them for himself. Michael decided he'd get them for him. He'd go up to the stand of spruce in spite of Zeb's terrible tongue and his mad dog. Maybe Zeb would be away. It was well-known that he hunted and trapped all over the hill.

The talk swung to the mine. How wonderful it would be to have the gold pouring out of the shaft. All of them were planning to buy stock out of their fish money. Maybe Ma Lovey was wrong, after all.

When they came to the glacier rocks, Lennie said, "O.K., Snapper! See you tomorrow." And all of them shouted, " 'By, Kiddo!" He felt himself one of them.

The oxen's bells tinkled over the ridge of the hill and were lost. Now that he was alone, he was conscious of guilt. What would Ma say about the trip?

Halfway across the hill, a shadowy figure rose from the shelter of the pine scrub. Willy! Willy was waiting for him. The boy's hands twitched with excitement. His eyes shone.

"Michael, can you read this?" He thrust a page of a mail-order catalogue into Michael's hand. Willy himself was slow at reading.

To Michael's surprise, the page contained an advertisement for patch work pieces for a quilt all "cut to size." "You thinking of making a quilt, Willy?"

"It's for Auntie Sammy, Michael. She wants awful bad to make a quilt like Margot's mother has in her best room. I thought maybe I'd take my money and buy her some patches. How much does a package cost, Michael?"

"It says one dollar and a half, Willy."

The light went out of Willy's face. "I've only got fifty cents. I'll have to earn some more." Michael thought, Willy is as fond of Auntie Sammy as I am of Ma Lovey.

As Willy turned to go, Joe Westerley passed in a car moving cautiously over the short cut across the rocks to Church Hill. Margot and Allwyn were with him.

"Hi, Michael!" Margot called proudly. And Allwyn boasted, "We've been to Halifax."

Michael knew that in the days before his birthday party and the fight, they would have taken him with them, and he wouldn't now be having this uneasy feeling about going home to Ma.

"Michael!" Willy brought back his thoughts. "Where's your plaidie? Did you lose it?"

Michael's hand shot to his neck. His muffler was gone! He looked quickly back across the rocks. Then he remembered. He had taken it off, with his coat, when he built the fire. He did not remember putting it on again afterward.

"Where've you been, Michael?"

Michael told him. His first thought was that he must go back and look for it. Then he remembered. Cy usually went up to haul his traps at this time of night. Cy would have found it. And whoever found the Cunningham tartan would know whose it was. They'd know he had been there—one of those who had taken and eaten the lobsters.

For the first time in his life, Michael was thoroughly frightened.

Ma had said he would get into trouble hanging around with Lennie and his crowd. Well, Ma was right. He had.

Only why did Ma have to be right? It was almost as if Ma, by thinking something bad would happen, had made it happen.

5. TROUBLE FOR MICHAEL

MA LOVEY was home when Michael got there. She was busy making out an order for drugs. For once she failed to ask him how he had spent his day. But she discovered very early the next morning that his muffler was missing, and her tone was sharp.

"I don't know what has got into you lately, Michael. You used to be so careful of your things. Since you've started running with Lennie and his gang, you don't seem the same boy at all."

Ma's words cut. They reminded him that Mr. Budd had thought him different. He had called him an American, as if being an American was something not nice. Ma could not yet have heard of Cy and his traps, but she seemed to guess that he had been with Lennie again. Ma didn't need to be so mean about Lennie. Lennie did things for fun. The lobster roast had been exciting. And what were a few lobsters? The traps would be full again the next day. Lennie was his only friend. For some reason,

Willy didn't count. It was Ma, he told himself, who was different. She didn't like him any more. Michael turned his back on her and grabbed his coat.

"Michael!" Ma's voice rang out.

He stamped noisily out of the house and raced down the hill.

The first person he met was Colin. Colin looked at him shrewdly. "Have you been up to something, Michael? Father wants to see you."

Michael thought, Colin knows. But Colin added, "Don't look so frightened. Father thinks a lot of you, Michael."

He was relieved. Colin didn't know then.

Michael went up to the house, and Colin's mother told him the minister was in his study.

"Sit down, Michael." The minister's voice was stern. He didn't waste words. "I'm much pained over this that I hear, Michael. Cy Sullivan is a stranger to this country. He lost everything in his own homeland, and he's trying hard to make an honest living among us." The minister knew then. "Have you anything to tell me about it, Michael?"

Michael stared at the floor. He couldn't tell without blaming Lennie.

"Cy works early and late," the Reverend Mr. Glendinning continued. "He's trying to get together a new home. The loss of the lobsters for even a single day is a serious matter with him. I am deeply shocked that one of my boys would do a thing like this to him."

Then Cy had found his muffler and knew he had been

there. Punishment was coming. But the minister's next words startled him.

"Allwyn Moorhans tells me that he saw you and Willy coming down the road from the direction of the cove last night. Is that true?"

"Willy wasn't out there," Michael said quickly.

"But Allwyn says he was."

"Allwyn is a liar!" Michael burst out. He knew now that Allwyn had struck back.

"I don't think that is quite the tone to use, Michael. But am I to understand that you were out there?"

"Yes, sir." Michael felt awful inside. He was afraid for himself, and he was terribly afraid for Willy. Willy had not been fully adopted yet. He lived in terror that Auntie Sammy might have to send him back to the orphanage.

"And you robbed Cy's traps?"

Michael hesitated. Robbed was not the word. He had thought the traps were Lennie's when he had opened them. But he couldn't explain that without telling on Lennie.

"I think, Michael," the minister's voice cut like lashes on his bare back, "this is a good deal more serious than you seem to realize. Whoever robbed the traps cooked and ate the lobsters and left the shells. The shells show that some were undersized. You are aware of the law and its penalties?"

"Ye—es, sir." Michael was thoroughly frightened.

"You do admit to opening and eating the lobsters after the traps were robbed?"

"Ye—es, sir!"

The silence in the room was broken at last by a heavy sigh from Mr. Glendinning. "This will be sad news for Ma Lovey, Michael."

"Wi—will they put me in prison, sir?"

The minister was slow in answering. Michael's heart seemed to be beating in his throat.

"That, Michael," the minister said at last, "is for Cy to decide. I don't know what he intends to do. Ma Lovey nursed him through a bad illness last spring. He doesn't want to hurt her. He may not report this. But he can't risk this happening again. You will give me your word that you won't repeat the offense, Michael?"

"Oh, yes, sir!"

Mr. Glendinning seemed surprised at the readiness of the answer. "I hope, Michael, this is not said lightly. I must confess this was a great blow to me. I always trusted you, Michael. I have tried hard to teach you that God does not love a thief, or one who consorts with evildoers."

"Yes, sir." Michael felt crushed. "But—Mr. Glendinning—"

"Yes, Michael?"

"Willy didn't have anything to do with the lobsters. He wasn't there. You won't let anything happen to Willy?"

"That's a nice spirit, Michael." Mr. Glendinning's voice was less harsh. "Of course, Allwyn might have been mistaken."

"Yes, sir. Mr. Glendinning, may I have my muffler?"

"I'm sorry, Michael, but Cy has it. He hasn't decided what he'll do with it. I suppose you'd be willing to tell Cy you are sorry you stole the lobsters?"

Michael scowled at the floor. There was that word again. He hadn't stolen anything. He just didn't know the lobster's weren't Lennie's when he helped take them.

Mr. Glendinning's last sigh was heavier than the former one. His voice became hard. "I'm sorry you feel this way about the matter, Michael. You may go now. Good morning."

Michael raced out. He felt awful. Ma Lovey would take it hard if they took him off to prison.

His mind returned to Willy. Mr. Glendinning had spoken as if he would forget about Willy, but would the other people in the village? How many of them knew what Mr. Glendinning knew?

He was trudging over the glacier rocks, kicking a stone ahead of him, when a voice called his name from the shelter of a scrub pine. Lennie looked out and Michael went to him reluctantly.

"You squeal on me about the lobsters, Michael?"

"Oh, no, Lennie."

Lennie evidently believed him. He looked relieved. "Good kid!" he said. Then his voice became wheedling. "Look, Michael, you keep your face shut. Cy's not saying much on account of Ma Lovey. John and Robert and Llewellyn don't know yet there's been any trouble. Anyway, Michael, it's all your fault."

"Mine, Lennie?" Michael was startled.

"Look, Snapper, if you hadn't left your muffler behind, nobody would have known who was out there."

This was a new angle, and Michael considered it.

"Michael, nobody knows you went out there with us.

Cy didn't empty his traps, for some reason, until this morning. Anyone could have been there in the night. Anyway, you're just a kid. They won't do anything to you. But Cy could put me into reform school if he found out I did it. You wouldn't want that, Michael. You'd miss your pal. Cy hates my father's guts. He thinks the wood lot belongs to him along with the cove he bought.

Michael wasn't listening. "They can't pin this on Willy," he said. "Willy wasn't there."

"Of course not," Lennie agreed. "Well, so long, Michael. And remember—no squealing!"

For the next few days every knock at the door sent chills down his spine. He was irritable and absent-minded when Ma spoke to him. Was the Mountie coming to take him to reform school? Ma Lovey threw many worried glances in his direction.

6.   A CRY FOR HELP!

FOR THE next few days Michael did his best to avoid the Mountie. He thought the Mountie might be looking for him, but not looking too hard, not hard enough to come up to Ma's and talk to him before her.

But the day came when he saw the Mountie and Scout walking toward him, on the high rocks, and there was no

escape from him. The Mountie had already seen him.
Scout was racing toward him.

"Hello, Michael." The Mountie stopped when he
reached him.

Michael said, "Hello, Captain MacKay!" He
reached down and greeted Scout. Then he glanced
quickly up the hill. Inside he had an uneasy feeling that
Lennie might be about and think he was squealing.

"By the way, Michael"—the Mountie put his hand in
his pocket and brought out the muffler—"is this yours?"
The Mountie held it out to him. "Cy found it," he added,
eying Michael shrewdly.

Michael grabbed the gay tartan. He felt light all over.
Cy wasn't going to do anything after all! Cy didn't want
to hurt Ma Lovey.

"You wouldn't want to tell me anything, Michael?"

For an instant the temptation to do so was almost more
than Michael could resist. He liked the Mountie, and he
thought the Mountie liked him. But—there was Lennie.
He'd have to tell Lennie's part in it, and the Mountie
would go after Lennie. The Mountie was the law.

"No, sir," he said reluctantly.

The Mountie called Scout sharply to heel and strode
off. Michael felt as he did when the sun went under a
cloud on a spring day and suddenly left him back in the
cold of winter. Something warm and friendly departed
with the Mountie, leaving him cold and alone.

Then the feeling passed, quickly as a cloud. He had
his muffler; he felt light as the wind.

With the new feeling came one of regret for the way he

had treated Ma lately. He knew he had been "difficult." But he didn't quite know how to explain his changed feelings.

Then something happened to bring back the old mood.

Immediately below him, Margot and Allwyn were playing with a bicycle. They were learning to ride. He had wanted a bicycle himself, but Ma had said, "No, Michael! Riding a wheel down these hills is much too dangerous. You're not old enough yet." And here was Margot, a girl, starting to ride all over the place. He considered joining them. Then he remembered that Allwyn was a fox. He was through with him.

Far down on the left, on one of the docks, he could see John and Llewellyn unloading a few buckets of bait. As he watched, Lennie hailed them. He was about to go down and join them when he remembered Ma's command. A little peevishly, he stopped. Ma didn't want a fellow to have any fun. The injured feeling returned. His own mother, he was sure, would have understood.

But the next thing he saw sent him bounding down the hill. In the lane beside Joe Westerley's boat shop, Willy was staggering along under a pail of water too heavy for him. I'm strong, Michael thought proudly. I could carry the pail for him without stopping to rest every two steps.

He found Willy on the wharf beside the stranger's car.

Willy was flourishing a big rag. "I've got a job, Michael." He sounded proud.

"Give me a rag and I'll help, Willy."

"Sure." Willy was pleased.

Together they sloshed the car with water, carrying many a pailful from the old-fashioned well in the field nearby. They scrubbed the car with the sponge and polished up the chromium and glass. When they had finished, the car shone like the cove water in morning sunlight.

"Sure is a beaut!" Willy said admiringly.

"We gave her a brand-new face." Michael had picked up the expression from Lennie.

"You think Mr. Budd will be tickled pink when he sees it?"

Before Michael could answer, the two men stepped out of the fishhouse and walked toward the car. Michael slipped out of sight behind some gear. It was Willy's job and he must get the full pay for it.

The two men got into the car and slammed the door. Mr. Budd, who usually drove, ran down the window and stuck his head out.

"Out of the way there," he shouted. Then he seemed to remember something, "Hey! Boy! Empty the bucket and put it in the back compartment with the sponge and the rags. Hurry!"

"Yes, sir." Willy threw them in and dropped the back down. The engine started. Willy had barely time to get out of the way as Mr. Budd backed the car a few feet in order to swing it around the corner of the boathouse into the lane. As the car roared away, two silver quarters spun through the air and dropped in the pebbles at Willy's feet. The car turned the corner, sped up the lane and away.

When Michael joined Willy, he was staring down at the silver.

The look in Willy's face hurt. "You think he did that, Michael, because I'm a Negro!" he said.

"Oh, no, Willy! *No!*" Michael knew then he didn't like Mr. Budd or Mr. Harte, and he wouldn't like them even if they made every villager in Portopeake a millionaire.

Michael soon found the strangers did a great deal of dashing about in their car. Whenever he saw them he recalled their remarks in the shaft house. He wondered what they meant by "fixing" Zeb, who lived alone in a cabin on the ridge. And why had it seemed to them lucky and a great joke that the Piper was walking again?

But he thought Zeb was pretty smart. He had come to the village the spring after the plane brought Michael. He'd been there almost as long as Michael had, and yet nobody in the village, not even Elmira McCabe, the postmistress, who managed to know everything about everybody, had ever found out why he had come or how he lived. Maybe Zeb wouldn't be as easy as they thought.

Thought of the hermit recalled the stand of spruce beside the cabin and Colin's need of bows. This would be a good day to get them. Maybe Willy would help him in return for his help on the car.

"Ma!" he shouted, rushing into the house. "Ma, I've got my muffler back and we're going up to get bows for Colin." Then seeing she was about to ask questions, he said quickly, "The Mountie had it."

Ma looked relieved. "I'm glad you got it back, Michael. And I'm glad you're helping Colin. You and Stephen and

Allwyn ought to think more about work. You can't play always."

"They aren't going," Michael admitted. "I'm taking Willy."

Ma looked surprised. But she said, "Willy is a nice boy. I'm glad you're friends with him, Michael."

Michael said, "Willy's a scarecat, but he's awful brave."

Ma laughed. "You know, Michael, I think that's an excellent description of Willy." Michael smiled back at her. Ma and he understood each other again. He felt better. Then he thought of something he had wanted to ask her since the day of the mine shaft.

"Ma, are Americans not nice people?"

Ma looked amused and then puzzled. "Why, of course, Michael, Americans are nice people. They're just like us. They speak the same language, and they have the same laws and much the same kind of government. They are our very good neighbors. You should be just as proud to be an American as Colin is to be Canadian."

"I'm glad," Michael said thoughtfully. As he raced up the hill, he decided Mr. Harte was just being personal.

Willy wasn't in sight when he reached the glacier rocks. He climbed the trail past Zeb's cottage alone. When he came in sight of the shack, he looked at it with interest. It was only a hunter's lodge made into winter quarters by stuffing the logs with moss and packing the base with sawdust. The wood was stacked like an Indian tepee, and the hen's shelter had a weather vane in the shape of a cock. Mallard ducks were waddling over the ground,

52

quacking noisily. He looked with wonder at the blue ribbon under their wings and the shining bronze lights in their necks. He had never been so close to a mallard before.

And then the silence was broken. Through the open door of the lodge came a wild, moaning cry, a cry that rose and fell with an urgent note, a cry that made him freeze in his tracks. It was the cry he had heard at the Piper's Pool when the ghost walked. Was the Piper here?

He was about to turn and race off when another sound hit his ear. From the cabin came a voice, a voice filled with pain, "Oh, my shotten shank!"

Zeb! Zeb was in trouble. He needed help.

With chills of fear running up and down his spine, Michael had to push forward against his will. Expecting he knew not what, he marched up the path to Zeb's open doorway.

7. STRANGE HAPPENINGS

THE SHACK was about ten feet from the path. Michael strained his ears. The cry was not repeated. But he still heard the squeaking sounds, as if a door were swinging in the wind.

When he reached the dark patch of doorway, his eyes were blinded and he could see nothing inside for a second or two. Then a voice that was quiet, but filled with surprise, said, "A mincing minikin! Come in."

Michael waited until his eyes became accustomed to the gloom. He knew that whoever was in the cabin, the Piper was not there. Zeb was stretched out on the bunk on the far side, one knee cocked up and his bare foot in a basin of steaming water which was on the floor. His hair was gray but it was thick all over his head, and his eyes were as bright as a boy's.

"Well! And who might you be?" Zeb greeted him. Michael caught a smile in the voice. That surprised him.

"I'm Ma Lovey's boy, Michael," he said.

Zeb scowled. "Ma Lovey's son is dead."

Michael nodded. "That's why she wanted me."

Zeb's face cleared. He looked almost kind as he humped himself higher on the pillows of the bunk until he was half sitting up.

"You break something?" Michael asked, eying the uncovered swollen foot.

"I did not. It's a shotten shank—a sprained ankle."

Michael thought, It's true what they say about Zeb. He uses bad words. "I guess it hurts," he said.

"You just bet it does." Zeb winced as he moved.

Michael's eyes traveled quickly around the cabin. Its neatness fascinated him. The walls near the stove were hung with pots and pans. Snowshoes, a gun and nets decorated the other side. Each thing seemed to have its place. Under the front window was a shelf of books, and an old high-backed rocker was close by. A young crow paraded back and forth on a rug, and his cry, Michael realized, was the squeak of a rusty hinge he had heard.

A restless movement on the bunk brought his glance' back. A black and white cat, front paws tucked comfortably under, had alerted her ears. Her head was moving from side to side as she followed the movement of the crow.

"Why doesn't the crow fly away?" Michael asked.

"I cut his wings," Zeb answered. "I like company—of a kind."

"I guess cutting a bird's wings doesn't hurt," Michael said.

Zeb smiled. His gray eyes were kind when he smiled. "Only his feelings, minikin, but—sometimes feelings can hurt worse than broken bones."

Michael nodded his head. He knew now that Allwyn's remarks about his parents had hurt worse than the blows he had taken in the fight. For a moment Michael and Zeb looked at each other in complete agreement. They seemed to have been friends for a long time.

"Maybe I'd better bring in a load of wood for you," Michael suggested.

"Maybe you had, minikin," Zeb agreed.

Michael saw that the water pail also needed filling and picked it up as he passed the bench where it stood. In the doorway he recalled Lennie's tale of a dog. "If I knew the dog's name, maybe I could make friends with him," he said.

Zeb uttered a harsh laugh. "That dog, minikin, that old

mumbudget, is called Beelzebub. He's a fierce fellow. You watch out."

Michael went out with the pail. Ma Lovey had taught him always to face anything he was afraid of. But he walked to the woodpile and on to the well with many a backward glance. "Here, Beelzebub! Good doggy!" he kept saying. He saw no dog.

Only the ducks ran to him excitedly, thinking his pail held corn. He saw nothing of the Piper either. He hardly expected to. Something told him the Piper was gone.

Michael filled the water pail. Then he brought in three armloads of wood. All the while the cat continued to eye the crow which kept up its funny antics. And Zeb eyed Michael.

Suddenly Zeb's head came up. "Someone's coming," he cried excitedly. "Shut the door and lock it, minikin."

Michael obeyed. Then he went to the window. He was curious. Who could be coming to see Zeb? Zeb's ears were certainly keen.

Then he saw in the pathway the rich coat and high collar of Ebenezer Budd. Was he coming to "fix" Zeb?

For the first time the low, threatening growl of a dog sounded close by. Zeb's dog was on the job at last. The growls rose into fierce barks. Michael pressed closer to the window, but he could see no dog. Through the glass his eyes met Mr. Budd's. For an instant they gazed at each other. Then a bloodcurdling howl, close at hand, rent the air. Mr. Budd glanced wildly around. And then, to the amazement of Michael, he turned and fled.

Michael swung around. The dog wasn't outside. He

was here in the cabin. The howls came from the bed itself. He stared at the bunk. The dog must be under the blanket which had dripped onto the floor. Then he saw Zeb's face and noted it was strangely puckered. His eyes glinted triumphantly.

"That fixed him, the old landraker," Zeb said, and a crafty look crossed his face.

Suddenly Michael knew. There wasn't any dog. Zeb imitated the dog growls to frighten people away. How funny! Everyone afraid of a dog that wasn't there. Michael flung back his head and laughed.

An excited squawk came from the mallards outside. "They're pretty tame for wild birds," Michael said. "They came right up to me."

"I tamed them," Zeb said. "Same as I tamed Desdemona, the crow there."

Michael said, "You're going to have lots of company soon, when they open the mine."

"What's that?" Zeb was sitting straight up now. Then he let out a groan as he shifted his position again. "They're opening up that old mine?" It seemed as if he couldn't believe it.

"That's why the strangers came," Michael told him. "To open up the mine. They found a new vein of gold."

"A new vein!" Zeb repeated. "That's a good one."

"But it's true, Zeb." Michael moved to the door and unlocked it. He flung it open. There was something in Zeb's face he didn't like and he thought he had better go. The eyes were cold and hard, and his thick tousled gray hair gave him a wild look. Anyway, it was getting late and he had to get the bows for Colin. All of a sudden he knew he wasn't going to tell Ma Lovey he had been at Zeb's. He felt she would not like his being here.

"I've got to be going," Michael said hastily. "I've got to get some bows for Colin's traps."

Zeb leaned forward. His voice was cold and compelling. "Come here!"

Something made Michael obey. Maybe the stories of Zeb's being able to cast a spell were true. When Michael reached the bunk, Zeb shot out a long arm and caught him by the shoulder. "Down on your knees, boy," he commanded fiercely.

Michael felt his knees folding under him, as his voice kept saying, "I've got to go. I have, Zeb."

"Now you listen to me," Zeb said as he knelt there. "You swear you'll never tell anyone I hurt my foot!"

Michael was surprised but he promised. "And you swear something else. You swear, you say, I, Michael Cunningham, solemnly swear—"

He was surprised Zeb knew his name. "I, Michael Cunningham, solemnly swear—" His face was as damp as Zeb's foot.

"I'll tell everybody—"

"I'll tell everyb-b-b-body." Michael tripped over the words.

"Kejimakujee is worked out, empty!"

Again Michael was surprised. He had expected something different.

"Swear it!" The hand on his shoulder seemed able to shake him like a puppy dog.

Michael swore it. Zeb sank back.

"Reach under the bunk," he muttered. Michael put his hand cautiously under the dripping blanket. There might be a trap there, an animal trap that would clutch and hold him. Instead, his hand touched something satin smooth.

"Pull them out," Zeb ordered.

Michael drew out five lobster pot bows, bent and polished and ready to use.

"There, minikin!" Zeb said. "Maybe that'll bring you back. I like company—of a sort."

"You mean I can have them to give to somebody?" He knew Colin would appreciate them.

"Listen, minikin! A gift is a gift. Now get out of here. Get going! Must I throw you out?"

Michael jumped up off the floor. "Good-by, sir," he said in parting. "And thanks a lot, sir. I—I hope your foot is better."

Zeb groaned. Then he started to growl like Beelzebub. Both of them laughed. "It's that Beelzebub inside of me," Zeb said. "I can't keep him down. I like company—of a sort."

Once outside the cabin, Michael's thoughts returned to the Piper. He looked about him fearfully. Was the Piper lurking in the trees, or had he returned to the Pool? Did the Piper make the strange cry? He must, Michael decided, for it always accompanied his appearances. Until he saw the Piper, he had never heard the cry, although he had spent most of his life on the hill. Fear overcame him, and he took to his heels and ran.

When he reached the glacier rocks, a small soldierly

figure was marching over the ridge. Cy was going out to his traps. Michael wished again the lobsters had belonged to someone else. He had always admired Cy.

Below him in the village the lights shone comfortingly. The days were shortening fast. He slowed his pace, thinking of Lennie. Lennie had said he had tangled with Zeb's dog. Why had he said so? There wasn't any dog. Lennie had lied and Ma Lovey had taught Michael that a lie was the worst sin of any he was likely to commit. Lies were so mean. Michael hated to think Lennie had deliberately lied.

No smoke was coming from the chimney of Ma's cottage, and he guessed she was not home yet. He had time to give the bows to Colin. Instead of crossing to the trail, he ran down Church Hill to the minister's house.

Mrs. Glendinning opened the door and invited him inside. She admired the bows. "Colin will be very happy to have them, Michael," she said. "It was thoughtful of you to get them."

Then he saw that she had a visitor. Mr. Budd was there.

Ebenezer Budd raised a monocle. "Young man," he boomed, "and what were you doing in that scallywag's cabin on the ridge?"

Mrs. Glendinning looked shocked. "Why, Michael!" she cried. "But I'm sure you must have been mistaken, Mr. Budd."

"Indeed I'm not. He can't deny it. Ask him."

Mrs. Glendinning regarded him reproachfully. "Is this true, Michael?"

Michael started to say, "Zeb hurt his ankle. He needed

me." Then he remembered his promise to Zeb. Why had Zeb made him make it?

"Yes, Mrs. Glendinning," he admitted and after he got the words out, it seemed to him they sounded defiant, so he following them quickly with "Good night, Mrs. Glendinning!" And raced away.

By morning, he thought gloomily, everyone in the village will be saying, "Ma Lovey's Michael is running wild. He spends his time in Zeb's cabin on the ridge."

Ma would hear the story. She would be hurt. She had never told him he must not go to Zeb's. She just trusted him to do the right thing. He had a feeling Mr. Glendinning would think going to Zeb's was "consorting with evildoers." Zeb used terrible words.

He wished he could tell Ma how and why he had gone to Zeb's. He wanted to tell her also about the Piper's cry on the hill. But he couldn't tell her. He had promised Zeb he would not mention the hurt ankle.

Michael opened the door of the kitchen and went into the warm room with its gay hooked mats and its wide window looking on the sea. There was no doubt about it; there must be something queer about being eleven years old. Ever since his birthday, he had done nothing but get into trouble.

8.   MIDNIGHT IN THE MINE

MICHAEL'S promise to Zeb was difficult to keep. When he insisted there was no gold in the mine, everyone wanted to know, "Who told you that?" It would have been easy to say, Ma Lovey told me. Ma had said the same thing. But Ma didn't like him to repeat anything he heard at home.

Colin guessed. "Zeb told you that, Michael!" he cried indignantly. "He would! He's been taking a living out of that mine for years."

Michael found the idea hard to believe.

"Look, Michael," Colin continued, "I'm not your brother. If I were, I wouldn't let you go hanging around Zeb's cabin. There's something wrong about a man who won't be sociable with his fellow men." Secretly Michael agreed with him, and yet he was surprised to find that he both liked and trusted Zeb.

Now and then Michael saw Mr. Budd or Mr. Harte in the village. Neither was friendly.

It was at the church suppers that he got most of his knowledge of what the strangers were planning to do. The women gathered there on Wednesday afternoons to eat supper and to patch and pack for their less fortunate neighbors abroad. Michael often joined Ma Lovey there for supper. The talk was all of their coming riches.

"Maybe there isn't any gold left in the mine?" Michael ventured, true to his promise to Zeb.

Ma frowned at him. She thought he was quoting her. But Elmira McCabe cried, "Now none of that ungrateful talk, Michael. After the strangers have offered to let us share in their fortune from the mine." Then turning to Ma, she snapped, "He got that talk from Zeb. Ma, you're neglecting that child something shameful. He's running with all the riffraff in the country."

Michael strode out angrily before Ma could answer. Zeb wasn't riffraff.

He thought a lot about Zeb. If his ankle wasn't better, Zeb would need wood and water. He'd better go back. He'd go on Saturday.

But Ma had other plans. "I told Colin, Michael, you'd help him with the fishing tomorrow," she announced Friday evening.

Michael was disappointed and angry. Ma had no right to plan his day without consulting him. A boy of eleven had plans of his own. It wasn't that he didn't like being with Colin. Colin let him handle the boat, and he loved the sense of power that turning the wheel gave him. But he hated the fishing. The lobster bait had to be overripe and it stank. Even soap and water didn't take the smell away. And the swells outside the cove made his stomach queasy.

"O.K.," he told her when she left at sunup next morning, but his tone wasn't gracious.

When he reached the wharf, the fog was rolling in so thick Colin wouldn't go out. Michael spent the day mending traps in the shack on the dock. It was evening before he could take the trail to Zeb's. Ma had sent word she would be detained until morning.

When Michael reached Zeb's there was no light in the cabin. Then he noticed a dark figure outlined against the closed door and chills ran over him. Was it the Piper? He got up courage enough to snap on his flashlight.

"Douse that light!" a voice commanded harshly. But he knew it was Zeb's.

"I guess your ankle is better," Michael said, eager to be friends.

"I guess it is," Zeb said shortly. Then he added, in a more kindly tone, "Thanks to your help with the wood and water, minikin."

The brief moment of light had shown Michael that Zeb carried an unlit lantern and a kit of tools. Colin was right, then. Zeb was working the mine.

"Are you going into the mine to dig for gold, Zeb?" He had to be sure.

Michael could feel Zeb staring at him in the darkness. "What do you know about that mine?" he demanded.

"I've been to the shaft house," Michael said. "Willy says the ladder goes all the way down."

"Look," Zeb said, "I'm going down into that mine right now, but not for gold, and you're going with me!"

"I'm not afraid of the dark," Michael said quickly. The idea of seeing the mine thrilled him.

"No! Well, we'll see!" Zeb laughed harshly. He put his hand on Michael's shoulder, gripping it until it hurt. Michael wished he were home. He wanted the comforting presence of Ma Lovey. Zeb was different—he seemed to have become a stranger. They started down the trail.

The ground was hard underfoot. Michael could make out the outlines of the trees on either side. There were stars overhead.

Twice Zeb stopped. He seemed to be listening. Then, just as they reached the shaft house, he whirled around and reached out into the night. Michael heard a startled voice say loudly, "I'm not doing anything. You let Michael go! You can't hurt Michael!"

Willy! Willy was afraid for him. Willy was a real friend.

"It's all right, Willy," Michael said. "Zeb is taking me to the mine. It's all right. I want to go down, Willy."

"Aye!" growled Zeb. "And since you're here, you young landraker, you can go down, too." He caught Willy by the shoulder and pushed him toward the entrance.

Willy squirmed but he couldn't get away. "It's dark down there. I'm scared."

"Nevertheless, you're coming! Listen, you young mazard. The mine's no place for youngsters. Those two carrion-eating strangers have got this village thinking the mine has walls of gold. I'm taking you down so you can tell them differently. Only don't you tell them who took you down. You mind that! This mine is gutted, empty."

Zeb went down first, but his hand never left Willy. He guided the trembling boy onto the ladder and helped him down. Michael followed. Darkness had never frightened him, but this was different. You could feel it around you like cloth.

A sudden jerk on the ladder told him that Zeb and

Willy had left it. The last two rungs wobbled weakly as he jumped off.

Zeb lit a lantern. A long alley stretched ahead of them. It sloped downward, and the rock ceiling was jagged and uneven. Silence was all around them; the air held a chill dampness, and now and then he thought he heard the sound of dripping water some distance away.

"Come along," Zeb ordered, stepping out briskly. They crowded close to him, fearful of losing him. "The other shaft is just ahead," he muttered.

Sometimes an opening appeared dimly in the side walls. Once Michael caught a whirring sound as of wings, and again he heard that dreary drip, drip.

"I hear water," he said. The silence bothered him.

Zeb swung the lantern aloft. His voice was a whisper. "It's down one of these alleys. If you go wandering about and get lost, you could drown down here. There are lakes and ponds in the old mine."

"I want to go home to Auntie Sammy. I don't like it here."

"Quiet!" Zeb whispered.

Then a new sound struck Michael's ear. A musical chink came from somewhere as if someone had dropped one tool on another.

Zeb heard it, too. He stopped, stiffened, holding them back with his hands. Suddenly he thrust them into a cross alley.

"Stay here," he commanded. "Mind—no yelling! And don't light your flash or move an inch."

Willy moaned, "You aren't going to leave us, Zeb?"

"Quiet, you mazard!" he repeated. Next moment he was gone.

Michael crouched down beside Willy. What if Zeb left them here forever?

"Michael," Willy whispered, "I'm frightened. I think I'm going to be sick."

Michael put his arm about him. He was a little that way himself, but he felt responsible for Willy. Willy had got into this business in order to help Michael.

"Zeb will be back, Willy," Michael said soothingly, as much to comfort himself as Willy.

The quiet frightened Michael more than the darkness. Once it was broken by a sharp crack and a rumbling like distant thunder. Was the mine caving in? He'd read in his school reader of such things happening in Wales. Again came the sound of one tool falling on another. Was someone working the mine? Was Zeb there to find out who it was? He wanted to believe in Zeb.

Willy, worn out, leaned drowsily against him. Michael thought of Ma Lovey. She would be worried if she came back and found him gone. He had no idea of the time. It seemed hours since Zeb had left them.

His skin prickled. Across the end of the shaft he saw a pale glow. Then he realized it was the beam of a flashlight. Was Zeb returning at last? Then he remembered Zeb had carried a lantern.

The small splinter of light crossed the opening again. Michael eased Willy carefully to the ground. Quietly he began to crawl to the opening, flashlight in his hand. Once he stopped to listen. There was still no sound of footsteps, but he caught the hurried pant of heavy breathing, and he knew someone was coming down the main gallery.

He reached the entrance. Zeb, he recalled, had turned off to the left, but the ray was coming from the right. It danced in the gloom like a string of fireflies. The breathing became louder. It was the breathing of a runner. The source of the beam was very near now.

It came even with him, passed, and with it passed a looming shadow. Only the breathing told him the figure was human. One thing was clear. It was not Zeb. Zeb had a light springy walk. The shadow flowed past, all in one piece. Michael was still watching it when the figure made a right-angled turn, and it and the beam disappeared. But he could still hear that labored panting and a little glow still lingered at the turn. He guessed the shadow or whatever it was had paused around the corner.

Michael recalled Zeb's warning, but Zeb wasn't here. He had to know what was going on around the corner. Zeb himself would want to know, some instinct told him.

Stealthily he crawled down the gallery in the darkness, his heart pounding. He came to the corner. He peered around it. The shadow had put down his bag. He had hung up his lighted flashlight on the wall.

Then Michael knew. It was *the ghost of the Piper's Pool!* He was seeing the same shining suit, the great feet wider and longer than feet ought to be. It occurred to him they were muffled and that was the reason for their silence.

But of one thing he was sure. This was no ghost.

Then, once again, echoing through the gallery behind

him, chilling his whole body, came the cry—the wild, awful cry that made his heart stand still inside of him.

Its effect was immediate. The figure swooped over the light, cutting it off. Blackness descended upon the gallery, but not before Michael had seen him snatch up his tools and flee, fortunately for Michael, in the opposite direction. Michael's heart beat fast as he started back, guided by Willy's cry, "Michael! Michael! Where are you?"

He sank down beside Willy, clutching his arm. The cry was followed by a deep silence throughout the mine. Even the cracks and the thunderings were still. He began to wonder about Zeb. Had anything happened to him? What would become of them if Zeb did not come back? Then his heart leaped. He had caught a muttered word. Zeb! Zeb was back!

Zeb's hand came feeling out for them. He spoke in a whisper. "Don't either of you peep! We're getting out of here! Keep that flashlight doused."

Zeb seemed in a hurry. He put a hand on their shoulders and rushed them back the way they had come. Michael thought of the open shaft, the pools and the lake, but Zeb seemed to know his way blindfolded.

At last he stopped. He pushed Michael forward. "Climb!" he ordered. "Climb fast!" And Michael felt under his hands the welcome rungs of the first ladder. Then the upper gallery and the second ladder. It was comforting to have Zeb protecting them.

Michael thought the stars never looked so bright, the air never felt so crisply fresh as when they came at last out of the shaft house.

Zeb turned on them then. "You didn't see anything down there. Neither of you saw any walls of gold?"

Willy shivered. "I went to sleep," he began. "And I dreamed I had lost Michael."

"I saw the Piper!" Michael said.

"What's that?" Michael knew he had startled Zeb.

"He passed the end of the gallery," Michael began and stopped. He couldn't see Zeb's face, but something told him Zeb wasn't listening.

"The ghost of the Piper's Pool—in the mine!" Zeb was muttering. "It's not possible, but then—maybe it is."

Zeb seemed to wake up then. "Listen, you two, you keep mum about this. You hear me. You promise you won't talk."

They promised.

"Now get home, both of you, before they miss you and start a posse out to find you. Scat!" Zeb left them abruptly and melted into the shadows of the shaft house. The creak of the ladder told them he had hurried back into the mine. Michael and Willy began to run. They didn't stop until they reached the bright open space of the glacier rocks, where the trail led off to Zeb's and Auntie Sammy's cottages.

Michael was in a hurry to get back home, but he remembered Willy's fears. "If you're afraid of the woods, Willy, I'll go up with you."

Willy said, "You go home, Michael. I'm not afraid of anything above ground any more."

They parted.

Crossing the rocks, Michael thought of Mr. Budd's

remark, "Fortunate for us the Piper is walking again," and the laugh that accompanied his words. Lennie had laughed that way when he had spoken of Cy's traps as his own. Had the Piper something to do with Mr. Budd and Mr. Harte and the opening of the mine?

Then he made a discovery that wiped out all other thoughts. Ma Lovey's cottage was alight. She was home ahead of him.

He slid down the hill and opened the kitchen door. Ma Lovey came running through the door of the living room.

"Michael!" she cried, and her voice was sharp with anxiety. "Where have you been? You scared me almost to death! It's after eleven o'clock."

"I—I've been out," he said awkwardly.

"Listen to me, Michael!" He had never heard Ma speak in a tone like that before. "In the future you must be in this house by eight o'clock. Do you understand?"

"Yes, Ma."

"Oh, Michael!" Ma cried. "Yesterday you were only a baby. Now you're running wild all over the place! I'm not the right parent for you." Ma burst into tears.

Michael watched her helplessly. He was stunned. Her tears hurt him, but they made him angry, too. Ma seemed to think he had done something wrong. She had no right to think that. He hadn't really. He had gone up to help Zeb because he thought Zeb needed him. And what did she expect a fellow to do, stay home alone all the time? Ma didn't understand him any more. And then a frightful feeling swept over him. Ma didn't want him any more.

He charged noisily up to bed. Why had his parents

dumped him on others? Was Allwyn right? They didn't want him. He didn't belong anywhere. Ma Lovey was tired of him. A dreadful thought hit him—if Ma Lovey gave him up, where could he go?

Then the warm, sweet smell of something cooking was wafted up from the kitchen. He recognized it at once. Ma Lovey was making him a cup of hot chocolate with marshmallows floating in it. She still loved him. He crawled under the bedclothes and waited for her step on the floor of the hall. He was comforted.

9. CALLING THE MOOSE

MARGOT got her bicycle. Now and then she let the others ride it. Michael was taking his turn on the high rocks one day when he almost ran down Mr. Budd.

Mr. Budd was startled. "Always in trouble, aren't you?" he shouted at Michael. The diamond winked as he flourished his right hand.

"No, sir!" Michael said stoutly. He had the same angry feeling he had when Allwyn taunted him.

"See here," Mr. Budd exclaimed, "you're the boy who is spreading the story there is no gold in the mine!"

"Yes, sir!" Michael faced him boldly.

Mr. Budd's gaze wavered. Then, "And who made you so wise?"

Michael hesitated. He disliked Mr. Budd and he hated his tone.

"Don't tell me!" Mr. Budd cried excitedly. "I know. It's that scallywag with the dog. You can tell that fellow you're so palsy-walsy with, he's living on mine land, and I own it. He may find himself without a roof one of these days. He better not tell any more tales and you better not repeat his lies." Mr. Budd strode off.

Margot snatched back the bicycle and Michael sat down on a rock. He thought over Mr. Budd's speech.

He was afraid for Zeb. Something told him Zeb loved his small cabin. True, on his last visit Zeb had seemed a stranger. And Colin said Zeb was stealing gold from the mine. But Michael thought of Beelzebub, and Desdemona, whom Zeb had rescued. Michael remembered the warmth there had been between them when he had brought the wood and the water. Zeb, he decided, was two different people. But one thing was clear. Michael liked both Zebs. And—he was going to warn him.

His chance came a little later on a warm day of Indian summer. He found Zeb sitting outside his cabin, whittling on a piece of birch bark. Desdemona was on one shoulder. The mallards squawked around, arching their bronze necks, and Nugget—Willy had heard Zeb calling the cat and told him that was his name—Nugget, the golden-brown cat, sprawled luxuriously over a nearby rock.

"Hello, minikin!" Zeb called and Desdemona opened her beak and cried, " 'Ello! 'Ello! 'Ello!"

"Oh, Zeb! You've taught her to talk!" Michael cried. Zeb seemed more wonderful than ever.

Zeb looked pleased. "I always aimed to," he said.

Michael settled down comfortably on the bench beside him. To his disappointment, Desdemona's talking seemed to be over for the moment. So he said, "How's Beelzebub?"

"That dog, minikin, is doing fine. Best watchdog on the ridge." Zeb lifted his head in the alert way he had when he heard something.

Michael saw that the Mountie and Scout were coming down the trail.

The Mountie sang out a curt "good day!" But whether it was for him or Zeb, Michael didn't know. To Michael's surprise, Zeb answered with the growl of Beelzebub. Zeb couldn't scare the Mountie, he thought. He needn't try.

But to his surprise he found that Scout seemed undisturbed by it. Scout came ambling toward him in the usual way, ready to shake hands. Then he rejoined the Mountie and they passed out of sight.

Meanwhile, it had seemed to Michael that a look had passed between Zeb and the Mountie. It was as if each said something to the other. Michael wondered. Were they enemies or friends?

"I believe Scout knows," Michael said when they disappeared.

"You think right, minikin. I wouldn't try to fool that dog. He's the law."

"Scout likes me." Michael's tone was proud. He was

beginning to think most of the village didn't like him any longer.

"Tell you a secret, minikin," Zeb said. "He likes *me!* That's two of us!" It seemed to make them pals, Michael thought.

"What are you whittling, Zeb?"

"I'm making a horn, minikin, a horn to call the moose."

Michael was excited. Some of the men who didn't fish went hunting in the fall. Joe Westerley was known as a "caller." Michael had not known the calling was done with a horn, but he recalled something that had always puzzled him. "I saw a moose once. He came right out of the forest and stood on the ridge, his antlers outlined against the sky. He—he looked like a king, Zeb." Michael felt excited anew as he recalled the long, funny face, and the gracefully poised antlers.

Zeb nodded. "If you lived in the woods, minikin, you'd know they are full of mysteries. A moose, for all his antlers, can run through the forest silent as a shadow, except in the rutting season. Then he crashes and thrashes like a hurricane through the branches." Michael knew the rutting season was the mating time. It was almost that now.

Zeb got up. He raised the almost finished birch-bark cornucopia to his lips. Michael hardly moved. Zeb held the horn high, then slowly lowered it in a great circle, as he sent his breath into it. And out over the sunny woodlands went a wild, haunting cry, a cry with a low moan in it. And Michael knew that he had heard the sound twice before, once at the Piper's Pool, and once, deep down in the mine. But the odd thing about it was, that now that he knew what made the cry, it no longer frightened him.

"Zeb, teach me to be a caller. Please teach me!" Michael pleaded.

Zeb handed him the horn. "It takes time and experience, minikin, before you can master it. Not everybody can learn. You see, minikin, one call doesn't bring a moose, you have to call several times, and when at last you hear him thrashing and crashing toward you, you have to muffle the horn against a tree. The sound must grow softer and softer as the moose nears you. It's an art, you see, minikin."

Michael raised the horn, and Zeb went on. "Point it to the stars. There's a bit of heaven in the cry, then swing it down in a slow circle until it points to old mother earth—there's a bit of earth in the call, too. Say 'eee-iiii-ooooo-uuuuuuu!' lingering longer on each."

"Eee-iiii-ooooo-uuuuuuu!" Michael breathed into the horn. A faint echo of Zeb's call rang out out over the hillside.

Zeb looked pleased. "Bravo!" he cried. "Someday, minikin, you'll be a caller."

Michael returned the horn and Zeb put a few final touches on it.

Desdemona hopped to Michael's shoulder. He sat very still. The crow's friendship, like Scout's, gave him an odd pleasure. But he wasn't still long. He suddenly thought of something.

"Zeb, why would anyone call a moose in a mine?"

Zeb's manner changed as it so often did. He put down the horn to frown at Michael. "You tell anyone about what you saw in the mine?"

"Of course not, Zeb. I promised I wouldn't."

"So you did!" Zeb became his old gentle self again. "And I guess you're a fellow who keeps a promise. You know, minikin, there's only one time a promise can ever be broken—if by so doing you can save a human life."

Michael was thoughtful for some time. Then he remembered why he had come. "I met Mr. Budd," he said.

Zeb's hands became still. "That's the old mazard who's going to get gold out of a mine that's empty!"

Michael hurried on. "He said I wasn't to say the mine was empty. He guessed you had told me there was no gold there. He said he owned the mine and he owned this land and—he'd put you out!" Michael was glad when the speech was over. Zeb was looking fierce again. He dropped the horn on the bench. He shot up straight. His eyes were blazing. Then he laughed, but it was not a happy laugh.

"The old mazard is getting scared. Look, minikin, you must run along. I have work to do." Then his tone grew kinder. "Here, lad, you may have the horn."

Michael didn't want to leave, but he accepted the horn eagerly. Zeb put out his hand and Desdemona hopped back to him. " 'By!" she said unexpectedly, and they both laughed.

That was the beginning of many visits to Zeb. Whenever Michael could, he stole away to the cabin. Presently he was taking Willy with him. Zeb seemed glad to know the little fellow who slid past his cabin so quickly each morning on his way to school. Willy had always been afraid of Zeb.

Zeb gave them wonderful lunches of bacon and eggs. He lived well, Michael noticed, however he got his money. And he kept orange and other fruit juices in a bucket in the brook. They were always cold and refreshing.

He usually had some project on hand. Just now he was damming the brook to make a duck pond. Between times he helped Willy with his homework, and Michael soon noticed that Willy was doing better in school. One day when they were working on the pond, Willy said, "Zeb, why don't you get some beavers?"

Zeb seemed unusually interested. "Willy, that's a fine idea." Soon they were watching a pair of beavers work. Zeb kept small sticks handy because winter was coming. Time was short. The house in the dam must be built under water before cold weather came.

On rainy days Zeb took them into his cabin. He got out an old bit of a blueprint of the mine. He traced for them his various wanderings, through its crisscross galleries. Here was a pond. There was a line of rails. Here a spring of water came out of the mine wall, and one could get a drink. Wonderful water it was.

Michael always had a feeling that Zeb was looking for something in the blueprint and one day he found out his suspicions were correct.

Zeb pointed to the legend of the map in one corner: (1) main entrance shaft; (2) the upper gallery, and so on. "This one," Zeb said almost as if he were talking to himself, "this one puzzles me."

Michael saw it was marked "tunnel entrance in the back of the hill."

"I've been all over that mine and all over the hill," Zeb said thoughtfully, "and I can't seem to find that second entrance. Funny!"

Willy said, "Where's the other half of the map, Zeb?"

Zeb laughed. "That, Willy, is another mystery. This was all that was left on the wall of the shaft house when I snitched it and brought it home."

The speech reminded Michael that Zeb was supposed to be stealing the gold. He acted, Michael thought, as if the mine and the shaft house were anybody's property, and so they had seemed for years. Still, the idea troubled him. If Mr. Budd owned the mine, the map was his.

Michael soon found that the best gift he could bring Zeb was news of the strangers and their doings in the mine.

One Sunday Mr. Budd electrified the village by going to church, sitting in the front pew, and putting a one-hundred-dollar bill on the collection plate. In order that no one might miss the gift and who gave it, he had neatly typed on a slip attached to it, "Ebenezer Budd, $100, his gift."

Michael told Zeb. To his surprise Zeb received the news with something like admiration. "I bet that got them!" he exploded. "The old skeesicks. He'd argue that the village would think him a rich man, a man who had already made a fortune, and they'd say he must be a good businessman to have done it, and they'd invest in the mine. I bet that got them."

"A good many more did put their money in the mine," Michael informed him.

Then Willy startled them by announcing, "My Auntie Sammy's got stock in the mine."

Even Zeb seemed surprised. Everyone knew Auntie Sammy had no money.

"She's doing Mr. Budd's laundry. And he's keeping the money to invest in the mine," Willy explained.

Zeb turned away, frowning. The black look had returned to his face.

There came a day for Michael when he could tell Zeb that the engineer's report on the mine had come. It said there was lots of gold still there to be taken.

Zeb was scornful. "That letter could be a phony," he said.

Michael nodded. Ma had said so, too. It was odd how often Zeb and Ma seemed to agree.

"And that, I suppose," Zeb snapped, "just about brought all the fish left in the pool into the net."

Michael understood. "There were only a few left," he said.

Zeb looked thoughtfully. "The difficulty, of course, would be to pin the fake letter on Budd. He'd say he got it in good faith and was fooled himself." Michael thought, Zeb shares my dislike of Mr. Budd.

Michael didn't miss Lennie or his own crowd when he could go to Zeb's. But he always went with a guilty feeling and only when Ma was away. He was so sure she would disapprove, and he was miserable deceiving her. But Ma had never told him, directly, he could not go. He lived in fear that she would.

The village openly disapproved. Elmira McCabe tried to make him promise he wouldn't go. He didn't answer. He just seized his mail and departed in haste. He knew she would broadcast the fact that he had been stubborn and impertinent.

One night, on leaving, Ma gave him a letter to post, reminding him of his promise to be in the house by eight. Michael agreed grudgingly. The evenings in the empty house were lonely.

He found the older crowd outside the post office, packing up to go on a picnic. Nobody paid much attention to him so he took out his horn and gave the moosecall. At once he was the center of attention.

Lennie demanded, "How did you come by it, Michael? Did Zeb make it?"

"The kid's darn good at it!" Robert said before he could reply. Michael warmed to his admiration.

Lennie snatched up the horn. To Michael's dismay, he pocketed it. "Zeb's darn good," he corrected. "And any horn that Zeb makes will bring an answer. Thanks, Michael, this will pay for the times I've let you use my radio."

"But—" Michael began. He couldn't part with his horn. And Mary Ellen cut in, "Oh, I say, Lennie! It's the kid's. Let him have it."

"That's all right," Lennie said. "Michael and I are pals, aren't we, Michael? Say, why don't you come along?

It's wild out on Slim Point. We might raise a moose!"

Michael jumped up. He'd go. Then he remembered his promise to Ma.

"Look, Michael"—Lennie guessed why he held back. "You can't be tied to Ma's apron strings forever. You've got to be your own man someday."

"I'm not tied to Ma's apron strings," he started to say indignantly. But he stopped. From the hill floated down the sweet notes of a bugle. Cy was up there. As the notes of "Taps" rose on the clear night air something happened inside Michael.

"I'm going home," he shouted and ran off up the hill. Maybe Cy would play for him. Cy might even go home with him. Ma wouldn't mind that.

Lennie's jeer followed him. "Ma's little sissie!" It hurt. Shame consumed him. He wished he had stayed.

When he reached the high rocks, Cy was gone. But his own gang was there.

"Zeb's at it again," Allwyn was saying excitedly. They were all kneeling beside a hole in the rock. Michael joined them. He had heard stories of the vents in the mine which opened into the hill, but he had never located them. Now he listened curiously.

"What's he working the mine for, if there's no gold there?" Margot demanded.

"We saw Zeb go into the shaft house with his tools," Velma explained to Michael. "The ladder creaked awful loud as he went down."

The sounds coming up the vent were easy to understand. There was the chink of tool on tool, as he had heard

84

in the mine. And there was also the harsh grind of a drill.

Why was Zeb working the mine if, as Margot said, and Zeb himself claimed, it was worked out? Why was he studying the mine blueprints?

Michael had a lonely feeling, as if he had landed on a rocky island and the tide had carried off his boat. Was Mr. Budd right? Was there still gold in the mine? Was it Zeb who was the villain, saying there was no gold there, that he might dig it out himself? The thought hurt.

10. FINGERPRINTS AND WHERE THEY LED

MA SURPRISED Michael the next morning. "Michael," she said, "tell me about Zeb. What is he like?"

Michael was glad his back was toward her and she could not see his surprise. Ma knew then. Of course, she was bound to find out. Elmira McCabe would make sure she knew. But he was glad.

So he told her all about Desdemona, the crow, and about the dam they were building for a duck pond, and about Beelzebub. Ma laughed. And he told her how Zeb was feeding Willy, and teaching him his homework after school.

"Zeb sounds like a good man," Ma said when he finished. And Michael was suddenly happier than he had been for a long time. He could go and see Zeb now without having a guilty feeling that Ma would not like his being there.

Then Ma wanted to know, "Does he use bad words, Michael?"

Michael hesitated. He wished Ma hadn't asked that. "They're kind of pretty words, Ma," he admitted. "They don't sound bad. I—I never heard any of them before."

Ma sighed. "Don't ever repeat them, Michael. And maybe you better not go and see Zeb too often."

Michael was sure Ma wanted to believe in Zeb. She hadn't forbade his going there altogether. He thought he had better change the subject. There was something he had wanted to know for some time.

"Ma," he began, "do you think my parents will ever come and hunt me up?"

Ma drew him down on the window seat beside her. "Listen, Michael, in my day I've handled a great many babies, little ones and big ones, and fat ones and skinny ones, and ones that have had care and many that haven't. But among all of them, I never saw a baby that had been so well cared for as you, Michael. Somebody had loved you very much. There is only one reason, Michael, why they have not come."

Ma paused. She seemed to find it hard to go on.

"Yes, Ma," he urged.

"Perhaps they couldn't, Michael. Perhaps they were already gone, otherwise they would have come for you long before this. You had that kind of parents, dear. The couple on the plane knew a lot about you, Michael. They thought it important to establish your name and age. I'm sorry, dear."

It had only been a dream and it was gone. Ma Lovey knew things when other people didn't. It was no use to hope his parents would come for him.

He started to ask other questions, but a tap at the door interrupted them. Ma looked up expectantly. It was early for callers.

"Come in!" she called. The door opened. Michael had a sense of guilty shock.

Captain MacKay stood there, Scout by his side.

Ma said, "Captain MacKay! How nice! You're just in time for a cup of coffee with me."

Michael at once sensed something different in the Mountie's manner. Today Scout made no attempt to leave his master's side.

"No, thanks, Ma! I'm here on business this time. Michael, where were you last night?"

Michael felt trouble rushing toward him.

"Did—did something happen, Captain?" Ma's face was white as the foamy edge of a breaker on the beach.

"Yes, Ma," Captain MacKay's voice was stern. "Some of the older crowd went on a rampage out on Slim Point. They broke into a house and tore it up and," he paused, "one of the crowd was a caller of moose. He lured a young moose into the open and shot him. It's closed season for moose, you know. A horn was left behind, the only clue."

Michael felt as if he had got lost in a swamp. There

was nothing to hold on to. Lennie had taken his horn. He must have called the moose. And they'd found it out, and were blaming him, Michael, for it.

"Where were you last night, Michael?" The Mountie's voice was sterner.

Ma's face frightened him. But he answered quietly, "I was home, sir. I came home at seven-thirty."

The Mountie turned to Ma. "Can you swear to this, Ma Lovey? Were you home, too?" The Mountie thought he was lying!

No, Captain!" Ma's voice shook. "But Michael always tells the truth."

Ma believed in him. He felt better. Something told him she always would.

Captain MacKay turned his gaze back to Michael. "Mr. Budd says you were with them. And you can call, Michael. I've heard you on the high rocks."

Ma's eyes flashed angrily. "Mr. Budd and Elmira are always picking on Michael!"

"Why should he say that, Michael, if it weren't true?" the Mountie demanded.

Ma and the Mountie both stared at him. Michael tried to remember the night. He had a feeling there was an explanation. "Ma asked me to mail a letter for her. When I got to the post office, the gang was starting out. They were going to shoot partridge, they said. They asked me to go along, but I'd promised Ma I'd come home at eight every night." And then something else came clear to him. "When I went into the office, someone was inside talking to Elmira. I'm sure now it was Mr. Budd."

The Mountie still looked solemn. "I think, Michael, you had better come down to the office with me."

"But he didn't do anything wrong, Captain," Ma cried. She sounded frightened.

Captain MacKay said, "If he didn't, Ma, everything will be all right. I'll get to the bottom of this."

Michael himself was thoroughly frightened now. The Mountie didn't believe him. The Mountie thought he had been the caller. How could he prove someone else had used his horn?

Captain MacKay opened the door for him to sit in the back seat. He usually sat in front with the captain and Scout. He felt terribly alone.

"Who was in the crowd, Michael?" the Mountie demanded as soon as they were in his office.

Michael didn't answer.

The Mountie crossed the room. "I'm going to take your fingerprints, Michael," he said. "There were prints on the horn!" Michael was uneasy. But he was interested, too. He wanted to know how fingerprinting was done.

"You see, Michael, if we could find out to whom the horn belonged we might know who killed the moose." And Michael thought, was it, after all, his horn, the one he had given Lennie? Maybe—maybe someone else had been out there calling. Still, chills of apprehension ran over him.

Michael watched the Mountie get out his ink pad. Then he brought a can of gasoline and a rag. He tore a piece of paper off a pad and laid it in front of Michael. He wrote Michael's name on top, his address and age.

Below were several squares. Michael saw "left thumb" under one square. He found there was a place for each of his fingers and his two thumbs. The Mountie, meanwhile, was talking. He was explaining how everyone's prints were different—even among members of the same family.

The Mountie picked up Michael's right forefinger, as if he were picking up a stick. He pressed it firmly on the ink pad, rolling it a trifle from side to side. Then he transferred the finger from the ink pad to one of the squares on the piece of paper. He rolled it lightly from one side, across to the other. Then he took another finger and inked and printed that one.

Michael gazed at the fingerprints. There were a series of little whorls in the smudge. He thought of the animal tracks which Zeb had pointed out to him in the soft mud of the brook bed. Everything left a trail, the Mountie had said.

The fingerprinting over, the Mountie took the paper over to his file. He seemed to compare the prints with something already there. Then he turned sternly to Michael.

"Your fingerprints are among those on the horn, Michael! How do you explain that if you were not there?"

Fear shook Michael. It was his horn! Lennie must have used it. Then something else struck him. If his prints were there, Zeb's must be there, too.

"Zeb didn't do it," he burst out. The Mountie looked surprised. "Zeb gave me the horn and—" He caught himself just in time; he was going to say, Lennie took it from me. Instead he said, "And I gave it to someone else there in front of the post office." He had an odd feeling the Mountie felt more kindly toward him.

Just then the telephone rang. The Mountie answered and seemed to listen a long time. At last he hung up, saying, "O.K. I'll be here."

"That," he said quietly, "was Mary Ellen, Michael. She confirms your story."

Once more Michael felt light as thistledown, as when he had got back his muffler. Mary Ellen was his friend. Lennie, he was sure, would lie out of the situation if he could.

"Michael." The Mountie wasn't through. "Why are you so sure Zeb didn't do it? The moose was killed by a crack shot. And Zeb is the best around here."

Before he could answer, a voice in the doorway cried, "The little Yankee is lying! Go up at once, Captain, and arrest that scallywag Zeb."

The Mountie drew himself up sharply. He said, "I am responsible for the law in this community, Mr. Budd, and I'll administer it as I see fit. Michael, you may go now. I have nothing against you."

Michael raced out. Ma Lovey would be waiting for him. She had been frightened, too. He thought, the Mountie doesn't like Mr. Budd any more than I do. He knew it by the way the officer had snapped back at the stranger. He ran all the way home. Ma would be interested in the fingerprinting. He couldn't wait any longer to tell her.

He was a little embarrassed when Ma threw her arms about him, almost as if she had lost him and just got him back. "And I've had my fingers printed, Ma!" Ma's grip on his shoulders stiffened.

"Oh, Michael! Why—why did Captain MacKay do that?"

"I don't know, Ma. But do you know there isn't anybody in all the world has marks on his fingers like mine, not even my own father!"

He wondered why Ma sank down at the table as if she were tired. He felt he must make something very plain to her. "I wasn't there, Ma. Honest, I wasn't. I wouldn't let anyone shoot a moose even if I called one, Ma."

"Oh, Michael, I know!" Ma answered. "But you get into so much trouble, sometimes I think I ought to send you away."

Terror struck at Michael's heart. Ma didn't want him any more. She was thinking of sending him away.

He was glooming about it on the high rocks two days later when the Mountie and Scout came by. The Mountie stopped.

"You like it up here, Michael, don't you?" His tone was kindly.

"Yes, sir."

"I wonder why, Michael?" The Mountie was looking at him keenly.

Michael found his feelings hard to put into words. But Ma Lovey had taught him to answer when spoken to. "I like seeing everything at once," he said and was surprised to find the words were exactly what he did feel.

The Mountie nodded. "It looks good, doesn't it, from

here? Well, Michael, we'll try and keep it so." They stood side by side a moment without speaking. Michael knew now that he had always pictured his father like Captain MacKay. But now he wasn't so sure. Sometimes he felt that the Mountie liked you only when you were good. But Zeb, he thought, Zeb would like you always. You could tell Zeb anything, well, almost anything. He suddenly remembered Zeb wouldn't discuss the Piper.

Michael turned to the Mountie. "Do you think the Piper could be a ghost, Captain MacKay?"

The Mountie looked startled. Then he laughed. "I'm quite sure, Michael, the Piper is no ghost. And I'm equally sure he's up to no good! See you again, Michael." The Mountie continued on his way.

Michael wondered what the Piper was up to. And how, if he wasn't a ghost, he managed to live under the waters of the Pool?

11. CY SULLIVAN'S BAND

MICHAEL soon discovered that not all the trouble in Portopeake was coming his way. Mr. Glendinning quietly announced from the pulpit that he was not using their recent gift of one hundred dollars

94

for a new roof, or for any of the other needs that had been suggested. He had already spent the money in his own way. A gasp could be heard from every corner of the church at once. Michael and Ma shared in the general excitement.

"Our young people in the village lack entertaining interests," he announced. "We can worship the Lord with damp heads, but we cannot save the souls of our young people with a new roof. I have bought several musical instruments, to add to those you already have. We will have two orchestras. One will be for the younger boys and girls, and one for the older young men and women."

Elmira McCabe was heard to announce, "You could have knocked me over with a wishbone! I couldn't have been more flabbergasted if Mr. Glendinning had put a bomb in the belfry, or opened up the cellar and pumped up the sea."

The village was in an uproar.

"The doddering old idiot!" Michael heard Mr. Budd say. "I didn't put my good money on the plate for nonsense like that."

And Mr. Glendinning, who overheard him, said, "Just why did you put the money on the plate, Mr. Budd?"

To Michael's surprise Mr. Budd said "Ah—ah—" in an embarrassed way and hurried off.

But Mr. Glendinning's action had one result. Elmira McCabe drew all her money out of the bank in Halifax and bought stock in the mine, and several others followed her lead. Many felt Mr. Glendinning was no longer a man with a shrewd business instinct.

Then Mr. Budd made an announcement. No more stock in the mine was to be sold. Men and machines were arriving immediately to start the work.

Only Ma's "tidy sum," as the villagers called her earnings, and the church funds, handled by Mr. Glendinning, were not invested. Michael began to worry. It would be dreadful if everybody in the village got rich and only Ma remained poor.

But Ma still declared there was nothing in the mine. And she backed Mr. Glendinning in his plan to have the younger generation perform together. She said it was a wonderful idea.

When the question was raised, Who would train them? Mr. Glendinning had an answer. "We have in our midst a trained bandsman, Cy Sullivan. He has agreed to train a drum and bugle corps."

Michael felt a thrill run through him. He remembered the pure sweet notes lilting down the hill. But he wished Mr. Glendinning had seen fit to class him with the older crowd instead of with Margot and Allwyn and his own gang.

The drum and bugle corps was to meet in the church house. Michael and Willy were the first to arrive.

"Oh, boy!" Willy exploded as he opened the door. In the center of the platform, neatly stacked, were the drums, with their bright lacings and shining trimmings. Nearby stood three bugles and an odd instrument in the shape of a lyre with crossbars. There were two round objects which Willy greeted with much enthusiasm as "Cymbals, Michael! They make a grand noise. *And* a triangle!"

All Michael's attention centered on the bugles. That was what Cy played on the high rocks. He could still hear the notes floating down the hillside. He moved over to a bugle and touched it reverently. Willy gazed in rapture at the drums.

Michael touched the bugle. Its shining smoothness was like the feel of a birch after one has stripped the bark. Gently he lifted it. The urge to try it was more than he could bear. But he wanted to be outside, on the hill, like Cy. He picked up the bugle and went to the doorway. He raised it to his lips. After two or three unsuccessful attempts, a note floated out on the night. He put down the bugle and listened as long as it lasted. When the last echo died, he tried again. Instinctively, he changed his lips, lifted his tongue. The note changed.

Margot and Allwyn and Stephen and Velma and the others stormed up the hill.

"Where did you get that, Michael?" Margot demanded. He waved a hand inside. They raced in.

Allwyn seized a drum and a couple of sticks. He began to pummel the drumhead. Margot pounced on another. "I can beat louder!" she shouted.

It became a contest between them, which one could drum louder. Willy tried to stop them. They never had paid much attention to him. They didn't now.

Meanwhile, outside, unheeding the hubbub, Michael struggled with the bugle. He didn't stop when suddenly the uproar ended in two loud reports followed by a moment of complete silence. Then Allwyn and Margot, followed by all but Willy, burst out of the hall and dashed past him, heading down the hill.

Michael had hardly realized what was happening. He had discovered the four notes of which the bugle was capable. And presently a weak, halting imitation of Cy's "Taps" was wafted out on the evening air. And Michael knew a joy he had never experienced before.

Mr. Glendinning and Cy, on their way into the building, paused. Cy seemed excited.

"You see, sir!" he cried. "What I said. The young people of Portopeake, they're musical. We will have a grand corps. A boy, he is either a bugler, or he is not. He plays it at once, or he does not. The drums now, that is a different matter. One can learn to be a drummer. All that is necessary is a sense of rhythm."

Michael followed them into the hall. He was a bit groggy with the joy of knowing he could play. He was happy, deep down inside.

Mr. Glendinning and Cy stopped in the doorway. Michael was filled with horror. Willy, stunned, was standing over the drums. Two of the heads showed huge gashes and on the floor lay a dented bugle.

Anger seized the minister. His eyes blazed. "How dare you do this, Willy Sammy! Music is one of God's gifts to men and you would destroy the means of creating it. Oh, why is this generation so bent on destruction?" Mr. Glendinning's voice carried a tragic note.

Sorrow showed in Cy's face, but his voice was quiet.

"One moment, Mr. Glendinning. Willy! This is not your work."

"Oh, no, sir!" Willy's voice quivered. "I didn't do it, Mr. Cy. I wouldn't do it. I played the drum in the orphanage band. I know. Oh, Mr. Cy, I can show you."

Cy held out his hand for Michael's bugle. He said, "Follow, Willy. I'll play 'Hail! Hail! The Gang's All Here!' "

Michael listened while Lennie's theme came softly and purely from the bugle. Then he looked at Willy. Willy's eyes were shining. He swung the drum sash over his shoulder. He attached the drum to it and picked up the sticks. And suddenly the whole room was filled with the steady rat-a-tat-tat, rat-a-tat-tat!

Now and then Willy raised a hand with its stick high in the air. Then both hands went up with sticks crossed. Both came down on the drum with a soft but sharp rhythm.

Willy was like something possessed. His whole body went into the motions. His face was shining.

Willy can play. He's good, Michael thought. Something deep inside himself thrilled to the music.

Cy returned the bugle to Michael. The drum gave a last flourish like a church "amen."

Cy said, "Your answer, sir. No boy who can play like that would ever abuse an instrument, sir. Someone else has been here. I alone am at fault. I should have warned you not to leave the sticks out. We do not give them out without instruction on their use. The drumheads are easily ruined, but they can be repaired."

"You think you can train them then?" Mr. Glendinning's voice had an eager note.

"I can, sir. These two are natural musicians. We will get the others back."

"And I can play the drum, Mr. Cy. You'll let me drum?"

"Yes, Willy. You can play the drum. We'll get you a couple of pompon sticks. You'll be the tenor drum, Willy, the leader."

"Oh, boy!" Willy sounded in heaven. "Auntie Sammy was going to buy me a drum when she got her mine money. That's why she picked me. She heard me drum."

Michael saw Cy look at Mr. Glendinning. The minister put his hand on Willy's head. "You tell Auntie Sammy, Willy, I'm lending you a drum. We," the minister's voice had a catch in it, "we'll be proud to have you in the corps."

When the village first heard the news of the broken drums, they said promptly, What can you expect? It was a fool idea anyway. And Mr. Budd seized on the incident to point out what a doddering example of impracticability the old minister was. Many prided themselves that they had not taken his advice, but had bought stock, and Michael worried afresh. How would Ma feel when everyone got rich and only she remained poor?

Allwyn and Margot and the rest were told the only punishment was to be a promise not to do it again. They came back to the practice periods.

On the first day of practice, Michael was very much disappointed to find the drums were not in sight.

Cy took the drummers first. He made them sit on the floor, Indian fashion. In front of each drummer, he placed

a board covered with linoleum. Then he handed each two sticks. Michael was surprised to find it was important how you held the sticks, and each hand held a stick differently. Stephen and Velma were slow at it, but Allwyn caught on immediately and Margot soon after.

"When do we get the drums?" Allwyn wanted to know. Cy said, "When you know how to tap and to stroke. When you master the flam and the long and short roll."

Then he had Willy play for them, pointing out how Willy stood, how the drum belt went over the shoulder, the hook in front. Much depended on the angle the drum was hung, and the position of the arms for firm stroking.

After they heard Willy play, they didn't care how long it took to learn. Cy let them practice with Willy while he started the buglers.

To Michael's joy, he gave them the bugles at once. He showed them how to stand also, and the angle at which the bugle should be held. "Mouthpiece in the middle of the lips," Cy ordered. "A third on either lip. The tongue against the upper front teeth, strain the lips slightly, leaving them together. Press the mouthpiece gently and not too firmly against them. Blow into the instrument as if saying 'too—ta!' Start sharply."

Michael practiced faithfully. By the end of the hour the notes were clearer. Cy took them each day after school. It was a red-letter day when the buglers and drummers played together for the first time. Under the clear notes of the buglers, Velma and Michael, came the rat-a-tat-tat, rat-a-tat-tatta-tat-tat of the drummers.

He found he no longer hated Allwyn. Allwyn was good

on the drum. And Margot didn't annoy him. They were all part of the band which was binding them together.

Michael spent many hours with his bugle on the high rocks. He wanted to master it.

Now when Ma stopped at the post office for her mail, on her way home from nursing, Elmira McCabe would say, "Michael and Willy were on the hill all day. Michael plays the bugle well and Willy is a grand little drummer. The music keeps them away from that awful Zeb's cabin."

Michael hadn't been to Zeb's for a week, although he missed him very much. Ma didn't ask him why but she often wondered, and was secretly relieved. Actually, there were two reasons. The idea that Zeb, after insisting the mine was worked out, was working it for himself, shocked him. Then, too, Michael didn't dare give the villagers cause for more gossip about himself. Ma might feel she had to send him away. Perhaps, too, the bugle was, for the moment, taking Zeb's place.

Meanwhile, the day that Mr. Budd had set for the arrival of all the men and machines to open the mine was drawing nearer. There was to be a great celebration. Mr. Budd even agreed the band might play.

One day the Mountie surprised Michael as he was practicing on the high rocks. He sat down beside him.

"Michael," he said, "I've learned I can trust you."

"I didn't call the moose," Michael repeated. He was still upset over that incident.

The Mountie, for some reason, looked amused. "I doubt if you could have, Michael. You see, Mary Ellen came to see me and told me the whole story. Lennie called the moose. He is an experienced caller, you know. But Lennie didn't shoot it."

Michael was surprised.

"No, Mary Ellen insists the shot came from the woods behind them."

Michael was puzzled, but he felt sure of one thing. Whoever fired the shot, it had not been Zeb.

"I've traced the gun, Michael. I know who fired the shot." Michael thought, The Mounties know everything. "But I don't want to prosecute yet. First, I've got to find out something and I need your help."

"Yes, sir," Michael agreed eagerly.

"I think, Michael, Mr. Budd has a typewriter. I'm not sure. But I don't know where he keeps it. I think he must be using some shack in the woods. If you ever hear the sound of typing when you're wandering over the hill, will you let me know?"

"Yes, sir." Michael was disappointed. He had hoped the Mountie was going to take him for a car ride.

"I notice that you and Willy wash Mr. Budd's car now and then," the Mountie continued. "Keep your eyes open for the typewriter. The time is getting short."

Michael didn't understand what he meant, but he didn't like to ask.

"And Michael, remember, this is between you and me. Don't talk to anyone about it, not even Willy."

"No, sir."

The Mountie started on his way. Then he turned back. "It's not in the mine, Michael. I've looked there. Promise me you won't go down there looking for it?"

Michael promised. He felt very proud. He had a job to do for the Mountie. Then he remembered something. Mr. Budd did have a typewriter. He recalled the one-hundred-dollar bill with its typed note, "Ebenezer Budd, his gift."

That typewriter must be somewhere, and he was going to find it.

12. MISSION FOR THE MOUNTIE

MICHAEL didn't lose any time starting on the Mountie's mission. The time he used to spend at Zeb's he now spent looking for Mr. Budd's typewriter. He went up to the shaft house and made a stealthy but thorough search. He climbed the rickety ladder to the loft. He found no typewriter, but he did find Mr. Budd poring over a tattered piece of blueprint.

As usual, Mr Budd was furious at finding Michael concerned in his affairs. "Don't you know yet that this is private property, you sly little snooper? You get off my land and stay off. I could have you arrested for trespassing, and I will the next time."

Michael hurried away. He had that chilly feeling he always had when he met either of the strangers.

In the course of the search, Michael persuaded Cy to take the band to Slim Point on a picnic. At least the band thought it was a picnic. For Michael it was a thorough search of the properties there. He slipped away from the games and roamed the woods far and near around Mr. Budd's cottage. He did not find the typewriter.

He managed to be around when Willy cleaned Mr. Budd's car. He boldly took the keys and looked into the trunk. Willy was shocked.

"Michael!" he cried. "You shouldn't do that!" Michael longed to share his secret with Willy, but he couldn't. Besides, Willy was friendly with Mr. Budd now. He still found nothing. Mr. Budd was smart, he decided.

He thought of all the places he had looked. Then he thought of Mr. Budd. Mr. Budd had spoken of the Piper as if he knew him. And the Piper had vanished into the woods beyond the Pool. Suddenly he had an idea.

"Willy," he said, the first time they were alone, "what's in the woods beyond the Pool?"

"Nothing, Michael, nothing but Cy's shack!"

"Cy's shack!" Michael repeated.

"Yes, Michael. Where he keeps his extra nets and mends his traps. He's too poor to build a house on the cove yet."

Michael jumped up. "I'm going out there right now!" he cried.

To Michael's surprise Willy said, "No, Michael, I wouldn't."

"Why, Willy?"

Willy frowned. "Somebody else uses it. He goes out there every afternoon."

"Who? Could it be Mr. Budd?"

Willy looked frightened. "I—I promised not to tell."

Michael felt sure then it was Mr. Budd. He would feel safe from visitors out there on account of the ghost. And Cy probably went there only at night after his hired work was done. Anyway, Cy was closemouthed. He might even rent it. Michael set out for the shack.

"You act as if you'd lost something," Willy said, panting after him.

"I have, Willy," Michael admitted, "but you mustn't ask me what."

"O.K., Michael."

They came to the shack. It was, as Willy said, filled with nets and traps and on one side was a workbench. Cy wasn't too neat. The place was a jumble. But there were no signs of the typewriter.

"You aren't going to take anything, are you, Michael?" Willy asked anxiously.

"What I'm looking for isn't here, Willy," Michael told him. He was desperately disappointed.

They were moving away when he noticed a large barrel with a bit of cloth poking from under the lid. Michael strode over and lifted the lid, pulling out the cloth. Something large and shiny followed the bit of cloth. For a moment they could do nothing but gaze at it.

Then Willy cried in panic, "Put it back, Michael!"

They were looking at the costume of the Piper of Piper's Pool! Michael knew then that the Mountie and Ma were right, and what he himself had suspected in the mine was true. The Piper was no ghost! He was a person!

They didn't find the pipes, but they did find the high boots that ended in the weblike feet of a duck, only they were two feet long and wide.

Willy stood back, afraid to come too near, but Michael picked up one of the boots and walked with it to the pond. He dipped it in the water and held it aloft a moment as the Piper had done; then he pressed it on the rock.

"Michael, it doesn't leave a mark!" Willy cried out. And Michael knew they had discovered one of the Piper's secrets.

But the costume didn't explain how the Piper could live under the waters of the Pool. The hat was no diver's helmet. Both of them had seen government divers at work widening the channel in the cove.

Michael put the boots back.

"Was that what you were looking for, Michael?" Willy asked.

"No, Willy. Oh, no!"

Michael led the way back up the rock. He crawled out under the trees and Willy followed. They gazed down into the Pool.

"You think we'll see the Piper, Michael?" Willy asked nervously.

"No. I'm just trying to figure out how he does it."

Willy frowned. "You don't think a ghost could wear somebody's clothes, Michael?"

In spite of his fear, Michael was amused. "No. I guess ghosts don't wear real clothes like those. Maybe we better go now."

But Willy held him back. He gripped his arm. "Michael, somebody's coming! Maybe it's the Piper for his clothes. Maybe he'll know and be mad with us for touching his things."

Michael lay still, listening. "I don't hear anything, Willy," he whispered back. How did Willy hear anything with the fuss the crows had suddenly begun to make.

"Hist!" Willy warned. "Something's bothering the crows, Michael!"

Maybe it was Cy, Michael thought. Then he knew it wasn't time for Cy, who went up the hill after his day of work. Was it Mr. Budd? Maybe now they'd hear the typewriter!

But nothing happened, and Michael was about to think they had made a mistake. He was just going to suggest going home when he felt Willy go tense. Then he too stiffened all over.

Something was moving in the green branches on the other side of the Pool. Something was pushing its way out of the grove.

Michael tingled all over. The Piper was striding toward them!

Willy crouched lower under the trees. "You think, Michael," he panted, "he knows us—and—he's coming up here to get us?"

Some of Willy's fear flowed over Michael. He held his breath.

The tall figure turned and strode toward the Pool. Michael was damp all over.

Then he noticed something. In the moonlight the figure

had seemed small and stocky. Now it was thin like a shadow. In the mine it had seemed to trudge, but now the gait was swift and free. The Piper had reached the edge of the Pool.

Some of Michael's fear left him. He edged nearer the cliff to see better. He was seeing the "ghost" in daylight for the first time.

The next moment a bit of gravel loosened under his hand and sped rattling down the face of the rock with a final plop into the Pool. With one accord, he and Willy slid backward under the trees.

The Piper's head went up like that of a listening bird. He raised his face and stared up at the rock. Michael shivered. It seemed to him that for a long period they gazed eye to eye through the screen of green.

Then the Piper spoke. "If you're up there spying, you old landraker, you better come down. I'm onto your schemes, and I'm nearing the end of the trail."

Michael and Willy gasped! The Piper was Zeb!

Down below, the Piper, apparently thinking he had been mistaken, turned to the Pool. He walked into it. Down, down, down, he went.

Presently only his head showed above the water. Then that disappeared, too. Michael followed his movements a moment or two under water. The Piper reached the dark spot below them, then disappeared.

Michael seemed to have stopped breathing. He lay there a long time thinking. The Piper was no ghost! He was Zeb! And Zeb had walked right into the Pool and gone down under the water.

Michael never took his eyes from the Pool. Zeb must come up again. He'd drown down there. But nothing happened.

Willy was the first to break the silence. "I didn't want the Piper to be Zeb!" he wailed. "The Piper is bad. Zeb's good."

Michael knew he felt the same. He got up. They went fearfully back down the trail.

But Michael's thoughts were racing. The mine had been abandoned for years. It had come to seem almost public property. Anyone might go in and take the gold. But the fact that Zeb was playing the Piper, frightening other people away from the ridge and the mine, seemed to argue that his business there did bear looking into. Would Zeb play the Piper if he hadn't something to hide?

Michael said good-by to Willy and went wearily home. He could see a light in the Moorhans' boat shed. The older gang was there. He wanted to join them, but Ma wouldn't let him. Then he remembered he'd got the blame for being with them even when he hadn't gone. He might as well go and have fun. Nothing mattered any more. Zeb was a liar. The Mountie had said the Piper was up to no good. Lennie had let him down. And Ma, though she loved him, he would never doubt that, didn't want the responsibility any longer. He might as well go down and join the older boys. At least he was welcome there.

Then he remembered his bugle. He thought of the band. Maybe if he became a great bugler, he could get on the radio and into television. He could hear the announcer saying, "We will now hear from the boy bugler, Michael Cunningham." And Elmira McCabe would say, "Ma did a good job of bringing up Michael." And Ma would know she did and never let him go.

He went into the cottage. He got his bugle and, sitting on the front step, he strove for the pure, clear notes Cy had sent ringing down the hillside. Happiness stole over Michael again.

13. DISASTER!

ATTENTION! At ease!" Cy was drilling his band. Michael was happy. He didn't mind being in the band with Margot and Allwyn and Stephen and Velma, when they all had something to do. Bugles on the hips. Bugles in front! Drummers with hands crossed behind their backs! Sticks high! Sticks low! Sticks reversed!

Cy gave the signal, an uplifted shiny baton. A rat-tat-tat from the drummers! Then the buglers took up the theme.

The band was giving its first public performance in a few hours at the Sunday-school picnic. They even had uniforms, little capes of royal blue with gold braid. And all the drums had CSB on them, for Cy Sullivan's Band. The mothers had made the capes. Ma Lovey had made

Michael's. Cy Sullivan's Band was proud of its uniforms. And Michael was sure Cy was proud of the band, although he'd never say so.

The picnic was being held on the high rocks, instead of out on one of the islands, because Mr. Glendinning said sadly, "It may be our last opportunity to go there. When the men and machines come to open the mine next week, the rocks will be no place for women and children."

Cy dismissed the band. "When I signal, you come! Watch the baton! Keep in time! Corps dismissed!"

Cy Sullivan's Band scattered.

Elmira McCabe singled out Michael and Willy. "If you two want to help, go up to Zeb's for another bucket of water. I guess the old scallywag won't refuse the church some water."

Michael let the remark pass. Maybe Elmira was right after all. Zeb was the Piper. His feelings toward Zeb were mixed. He still longed to believe in him. He hadn't seen him since he had discovered he was the Piper! He felt embarrassed.

The moment they came in sight of the shack, Michael knew something was different. A bulging knapsack and a hatchet stood by the doorway. Over everything was a strange silence. The ducks were nowhere in sight. Zeb came striding out of the door with his gun. He looked different. It was plain he was ready to travel. He was carefully shaved, but Michael sensed Zeb was heading for the bush. Every year it was his custom to disappear for several weeks.

"Zeb!" Michael cried, everything else forgotten. "Oh, Zeb! You're going away!"

Willy stared his unbelief.

Zeb smiled at the anxious tone and Michael again felt the old spell.

"Sorry, minikin. The time has come to move on. I thought you'd gone away yourself."

Michael was hurt. Zeb was really going, going for good, not just into the bush. And he was going without saying good-by. "I—I've been busy," he said awkwardly. Something rose in his throat. He'd miss Zeb.

"Elmira wants a bucket of water," Willy filled in the silence.

"She can have it," Zeb said. He took out his pipe and filled it in leisurely fashion. "I guess Elmira can wait for once. Have a visit. I'm not going just yet." Zeb sat down on the bench. Michael dropped down on Nugget's rock. The cat was nowhere about.

Suddenly he knew why it was so silent. "Where are Desdemona and the mallards?" he demanded. "Where's Nugget?"

"I took them up to Auntie Sammy's this morning," Zeb said. "I thought Willy might like to have them."

"Oh, boy!" Willy breathed. "I better run home. Desdemona might be lonesome. I'll be back in a minute, Michael." Willy ran away.

Michael was hurt anew. Zeb had given the talking crow to Willy. He'd thought of Willy but not of him! Zeb didn't like him any more. He felt shy and awkward. He couldn't think of anything to say. Then he remem-

114

bered something he wanted to ask Zeb. It was a silly question but Ma wanted to know, too.

"When you hurt your foot, Zeb, why didn't you want the village to know?"

Zeb's laugh rang out, but it was followed quickly by a frown. "Look, minikin! I was sick once. And the villagers of Portopeake found out. You know what happened, minikin? Six of those mumbling giglets skimble-scrambled up here! And you know what they did?"

"What, Zeb?"

"They packed me off to the hospital. Then they started to clear away the place. They began burning up my things. They'd have done it, too, only the Mountie found out. He sent them skittering. He locked up the cabin. I've steered clear of Portopeake ever since." Zeb suddenly dismissed the matter. "What's new, minikin?"

"They're opening the mine," Michael told him, "next week." But for once the news had already reached Zeb.

"Yes, that's Budd's story," he said.

Then Willy returned. "Desdemona was awful glad to see me, Zeb. I gave her some water. The mallards were in the pond. I like their talk. It's company. Michael and me, Zeb, we'll take awful good care of Desdemona." Michael felt better. Willy was sharing with him.

Zeb put down his pipe. "I know you will, Willy. Well, time's getting short. There's orange juice in the brook. I kept it—for company! We'll have a cup, then I must be on my way."

They went into the cabin for the porcelain cups. Michael saw that everything was all packed up. Zeb was going! He had to believe it. Then a shadow darkened the doorway. Michael was startled to see Mr. Glendinning standing there.

Zeb looked around. His anger returned. "You skimble-scramble out of here, you old landraking misprized minimus."

Then Michael got a real surprise. Mr. Glendinning threw back his head in a laugh that was almost a shout. "Sithen I'm here, you motley-minded one, 'tis no occasion to be so roynish!"

Michael was shocked. But the anger died out of Zeb's face. A slow smile changed it.

"Oh, Zeb," Mr. Glendinning cried, "I know my Shakespeare, too. English was a sturdy language in those days."

"But aren't they—bad words?" Michael demanded.

"No, Michael! They're just what we call archaic words. Words so old people have forgotten them. I tumbled to what they were the moment I really heard you speak, Zeb." Zeb nodded. He looked pleased.

Then Mr. Glendinning sobered. "I came to ask you a question, Zeb. Is there any gold in the mine?"

"Not a nugget, sir," Zeb said. "I've been sending samples away for a year. There's nothing left that would pay for the digging and Budd knows it." So that was what Zeb had been doing, Michael thought. He hadn't been stealing. He'd been proving what Ma Lovey always said, there was nothing in the mine! Zeb wasn't a thief! Michael was happier than he had been for a long time.

"But I saw gold, a whole vein of it," Mr. Glendinning said.

"It was planted there for you to see, sir. The Mountie and I knew they were planting it, but we couldn't catch them at it." Michael thought, Zeb and the Mountie were working together. They were friends.

"And the report of the engineers?"

"Fake!" Zeb announced. "The Mountie checked with the firm on whose letterhead it was written, and they never sent it. We think Mr. Budd wrote it himself, after getting the firm's paper, somehow. But he'll claim, of course, he was fooled, too. Unfortunately, we can't prove he wrote it yet."

"But something should be done," Mr. Glendinning said anxiously.

"And quickly," Zeb agreed.

Just then Elmira's voice reached them faintly. "Michael! Wil—ly! Where are you?" Willy jumped up and raced off to the well with the bucket.

"Dear me!" said Mr. Glendinning. "I had almost forgotten the picnic. I would like to ask you to join us."

Zeb smiled. "And face Elmira, padre! Elmira thinks I'm a mean old scallywag! Thank you, sir, but I'm pulling out."

"I'm sorry." Mr. Glendinning sounded as if he meant it. "It's hard to lose a friend, even a recent one."

"Thank you again, sir!" The two men shook hands. Zeb wasn't a thief, Michael thought. And he didn't swear. He was going just when they could be friends.

The cabin door banged behind them. Zeb locked it. Mr. Glendinning started down the trail. Willy and Michael stood very still. Zeb shouldered his knapsack. He picked up the hatchet and the gun. He nodded a farewell. Then he strode off. The woods swallowed him. Zeb was gone!

Michael felt as if he had lost his bugle. Then something occurred to him. "Oh, Willy, we never told him about the band!" It seemed terrible that Zeb had gone without knowing.

"Don't you 'spose he heard us?" Willy questioned, and Michael thought there were many things about the band that Zeb could hear only if he were told.

They took the water to Elmira and were reminded of their delay.

"Let's go up on the high rocks, Willy," Michael suggested. He had an urge to play. "We could practice."

Willy swung his drum sash over his shoulder and attached the drum. Michael shouldered his bugle. They started up toward the shaft house.

They found Robert and Colin and the older crowd already there. The big boys were starting down the ladder to the mine.

Colin cried, "Go back, Michael! If you go down, they'll all follow." Looking down the trail, Michael saw the rest of the band had followed up the hill.

The older boys did not stay down. They climbed back immediately. Robert called, "Don't anybody go down that ladder. It's not safe." They moved off into the woods.

Margot tossed her head. "I'm not afraid!" she cried scornfully.

"But Robert says it's not safe, Margot," Michael warned.

"I don't like the ladder!" Stephen cried. "I don't want to go down."

"Who's afraid!" Margot taunted and entered the building.

Allwyn trailed close behind. "You're not going to let a girl call you scarecat, Stephen, are you?" he shouted.

Michael turned to Willy. He said, "They're just showing off. Come on! If we leave, they won't go down."

He led the way up to the jagged rocks and Willy followed, a little doubtfully. Once at the top they flung themselves down flat on their stomachs and considered the scene below. It was like a play. The women were still setting the tables. The men were making the fires. The babies were playing tag around their mothers' skirts. They could see it all.

As usual, Michael found his thoughts wandering. Zeb was gone. Already his world seemed empty without him. Zeb would become a shadowy figure like the father and mother whom he had never known. He had come to accept the fact, as Ma Lovey had, that he would never see his parents, but he still wondered, in odd moments, how and why he had been put on the plane that cracked up in Portopeake on Christmas Eve.

"There's Mr. Budd!" Willy said suddenly. He sounded surprised.

Michael saw him, too. He shared Willy's surprise. Mr. Budd seemed to be acting rather oddly. He had come out from under the trees with a carriage rug in his arms and a satchel and bundles. What was he up to?

Michael and Willy watched him with curiosity.

As Mr. Budd neared the long sloping back roof of the shaft house, he threw the rug up on it. For a moment Michael thought he must be going to lie down there. He and Willy had done that many a time, seeking a warm shelter on a windy day.

But Mr. Budd didn't get up on the roof, although he spent some minutes bending over the rug as if he were arranging it to his taste. A few seconds later they saw him moving hurriedly around the house. He had reached the corner when Desdemona came skittering out of the bushes crying, " 'Ello! 'Ello! 'Ello!" She must have followed Willy down.

Mr. Budd's reaction struck both Michael and Willy as terribly funny. He jumped almost out of his skin. He gave a wild glance around in all directions, spotted Desdemona, and, dropping the leather case he was carrying, chased after the bird. His gestures showed he was very angry. Desdemona disappeared into the bushes, and Mr. Budd, with a last defiant wave of his arm in her direction, returned, picked up the satchel and vanished through the front door of the shaft house. But in a second he was out again, minus papers and satchel. He seemed to have left them behind. Why? The next moment Mr. Budd was sprinting up the trail, to disappear like Desdemona into the bushes along its edge.

Michael was puzzled.

Then Willy spoke. "He left the little case behind, Michael. He's awful careful of it. He keeps it in a secret closet in the cushion under the driver's seat of his car. Mr. Budd is clever, nobody would ever find it there. It's the littlest typewriter you ever saw. He says it's a foreign make."

Michael stared at him. Willy—Willy had known all the time what the Mountie had been so eager to learn—where Mr. Budd kept his typewriter!

Then he jumped to his feet. Mr. Budd might have parked the case in the shaft house for only a few minutes. He might come back for it. Michael must find the Mountie and tell him right away.

He hurried down the rocky trail, Willy crying behind him, "Michael! Michael! What's the matter?"

Michael turned and ran back into the dark interior of the shaft house and stood there puzzled. The case was nowhere in sight!

Willy came panting in behind him. "What is it, Michael?" he repeated.

Michael said, "The satchel! Willy, I must have it."

And then a sound came to them both.

Voices rose from the shaft. They were shouting his name. "Michael! Colin! Help! We—we can't get up."

Margot and the band!

Margot must have gone down into the mine and taken the others with her. His first thought was that if she had got into trouble, it served her right. She should not have gone down when Colin and Robert had said not to.

And then he heard the voices again. This time he realized they sounded badly frightened. "Michael! Michael! We can't get up! The ladder is broken." They had caught Willy's voice.

So that was what had happened. "Listen," he shouted down impatiently, "if the ladder is broken, I'll have to go for help. Stay where you are, and we'll get you up."

Willy had moved outside. Willy was excited. He was staring up at the roof. "Michael! Look!" he turned to see what had startled Willy.

Amazement struck him. The top of the shaft house was smoking. And even as he looked, a shower of sparks, like golden snowflakes, sailed off in the breeze. He turned again to the inside. High in the old roof a red glow was spreading. Smoke, like a fog, had gathered among the rafters. His eyes began to smart. Then he understood what had happened. The whole shaft house was on fire and it was old, dry, and rickety. In a few minutes it would be a torch. He must get help. Willy wouldn't do. This was a man's job. A red-hot cinder broke from the roof and fell smoking on the floor. There would be others and they would go down, all the way down, upon Allwyn and Margot and Stephen and Velma. What if they panicked and started to run! He thought of the ponds and lakes in the mine. Only he and Willy knew the mine and Willy would be afraid to go down. He was afraid himself.

The fire overhead was roaring up now. The voices below sounded more frantic. "Michael! Hurry! We're afraid! Help us!"

"Willy," he found his voice, "Willy, get help! Margot's in the mine and the ladder is broken."

He told himself he couldn't go down. He had promised the Mountie he wouldn't. Then he saw Zeb, Zeb telling him, "You can only break a promise, Michael, to save a life." Then Ma Lovey warning him, "You have an honored name, Michael. You must be brave."

With the roaring overhead, there was mingled now a snapping sound. Pieces of the roof were falling.

The band rose before him in a picture, Cy Sullivan's Band, only now there were just two of them in it, himself and Willy.

The mind pictures exploded in a single flash. "I'm going down!" he shouted. "Stand away from the shaft, Margot. I'm coming."

"No, Michael! No, you can't." Willy's voice reached him through the noise and the smoke. Willy hadn't gone for help!

"Willy, get help!" he shouted again and flung himself down on the ladder. Down! Down! It seemed endless. Was the ladder completely gone, or had the last few rungs slipped out? He recalled they had seemed weak when he went down with Zeb. Maybe he could slide the last few feet.

Down! Down! Down! A red light filled the well as a burning brand just missed him. A lonely feeling crept over him. He seemed to be leaving everything behind— Ma, Zeb, Willy, the Mountie, and Scout. Then Mr. Glendinning's voice came to him, "Yea, though I walk through the valley of the shadow . . . thy rod and thy staff . . . they comfort me." The loneliness left him.

The roar overhead seemed to be pursuing him down. Something big and heavy was almost on top of him. His feet missed the rungs. He found himself plunging downward with burning palms. Then his feet hit solid ground. He moved away from the shaft just as the dark object dropped beside him, narrowly missing him.

"I had to come, Michael," a voice said.

Willy! Willy had followed him down! They were lost!

Willy's voice came again through the gloom. "They'll see the flames, Michael. Margot left her drum at the door of the shaft house. They'll understand!"

Willy had thought fast. Suddenly he was glad to have Willy beside him. Maybe everything would be all right yet.

"Michael! Michael!" Margot's hand sought his. He could feel the others crowding closer. "Oh, Michael, what's happening? What will we do?"

His first thought was to herd them away from the bottom of the shaft. Then he explained about the fire. Sooner or later they'd have to know. But he hadn't finished speaking when a rumbling roar started in the darkness. A great light illumined their white frightened faces. And then followed a long, slow, terrifying crumbling crash, which seemed to grow louder and louder as it rushed toward them, a roar made up of thousands of splintering little sounds. The light blacked out.

And Michael guessed, with fear in his heart, that part of the earth around the shaft mouth had given way and fallen into the shaft. The fire below was out! But—they were sealed into the earth!

14. SEALED IN THE MINE

A SPASM of choking attacked them all. Michael felt for his flashlight. It was always in his pocket. Now he turned its beam on the shaft opening. Willy gasped, and Michael swung it quickly away again. The shaft well was choked with a mass of smoking timbers. The ash dust was getting into their throats. He felt small and helpless.

"Michael, we've got to move on!" he urged. Michael knew by Willy's voice he was scared. But he knew he was right. Willy was keeping his head.

Michael herded them cautiously down the gallery, keeping the lead himself. A sharp cry made him turn back quickly. Willy had stumbled and fallen. Michael's heart almost stopped. He needed Willy.

"It's—it's all right, Michael!" Willy panted. He was up again. Michael sent the beam of his flashlight ahead. He tried to recall the blueprint. Zeb had said there was another entrance and had traced the beginning of it on the half of the map that he had.

But now the white lines of the blueprint seemed very different from these dark alleys. Somehow he had to find that entrance. He had to get them out.

Then a weak voice he knew for Stephen's said, "Michael, it hurts. I fell off the ladder. My ankle hurts. I—I

can't walk—any more." Stephen's voice ended in a wail.

Margot answered through the darkness. "We'll make a chair and carry you, Stephen. Allwyn and I will take first turn. Michael and Willy have to lead the way."

Slowly he made his way down the main gallery. Would they balk at going down deeper into the mine?

His flashlight was the kind that makes its own electricity. He had to work it to keep the flash going. But it would never go out. Ma Lovey had given it to him. Odd how she always foresaw his needs. She had been a real mother to him, he knew now.

At the first halt he turned the flashlight on the gang. Their faces were white, their eyes large with fright, but no one was crying.

"Listen!" he said. "The mine runs across the whole top of the ridge. There's a second opening which comes out on the far side of the hill above Cameronia. We—we're going out that way."

"I think we ought to stay near the main shaft till help comes," Allwyn said. Michael caught a stubborn note in his voice.

"But Allwyn, that might take days. The shaft is completely blocked," he said. "We might reach the other opening in a few hours."

"How do you know so much, Michael Cunningham?" Allwyn demanded.

Willy answered for him. "Michael and I," he said confidently, "we've been in the mine before."

"See, Allwyn," Margot announced. "Michael knows. Come on!"

Michael thought, It's Willy who is the real leader.

"O.K. Forward march!" he ordered. He tried to make his voice sound like Cy's.

Carrying Stephen slowed them down. Zeb's words about the mine kept ringing through his head. The galleries were full of lakes and ponds. People could get drowned there.

Then a new fear faced Michael. The road ahead was blocked. For a moment he was cold inside. Some of the roof had fallen. But Willy discovered there was still room for them to wedge themselves around the boulder. Somehow they did it.

Michael knew they must get to the lower level. Zeb had warned that vibrations in a mine were bad. The roar of the falling shaft house had been terrific.

As they moved ahead, he prepared the band for the second shaft. When the black hole opened abruptly before them, not even Allwyn balked.

The big problem was getting Stephen down the ladder. Willy, as usual, found a way. He took Stephen on his back. Then he kept so close to Michael, who went ahead, that Stephen was like a sandwich between them.

Michael was happier when they were all down and the last rung of the ladder was behind him. His foot touched gratefully the gravelly rock of the gallery floor. He had feared that this ladder, too, might have collapsed.

"The second opening into the mine," he told them, quoting Zeb, "isn't a shaft like these two. It's a tunnel. The gallery comes out in the side of the hill. We'll find that tunnel and walk out." He tried to make his voice sound as if he knew what he was telling them. Inside, he was quaking.

"It's my turn with the flashlight," Allwyn suddenly insisted. Michael had been expecting trouble from Allwyn.

But it was Margot who objected. "Michael and Willy know the way, Allwyn," she cried sharply. And Michael was glad when Willy took the flashlight from him. His own hand ached horribly.

They trudged valiantly on through the shadows. Michael's mind went back to the blueprint. The entrance was on the other side of the ridge according to Zeb. The Piper's Pool was on the other side, too. It had not always been a pool. Ma said the hollow had once been an old quarry. Zeb had been troubled because he could not find the other opening into the mine, but the last time they studied the map, Michael was sure that Zeb had known the gallery that led to it.

Zeb had muttered something about it's having been there all the time right under his nose, but he hadn't seemed to want to talk further. He had ended by saying that using your head was often as good as knowing the way to something.

It was then a wild thought struck Michael. He had seen the Piper in the Pool. He had seen him in the mine. Was it possible the entrance came out in the old quarry? If it did—a horrid thought struck him—it would now be under water. A shiver ran over him. Maybe the Piper did not come out of the waters of the Pool; maybe he came *through* them!

Terror seized him. If the entrance was under water,

they were lost. He was glad of the darkness. The others could not see his fright.

Then he remembered a saying of Ma's. "Troubles in the future have a way of disappearing when you reach them, Michael. Keep your mind on the job at hand." But how would he know when he got to the entrance if the waters of the Pool covered the top of the opening?

At the next halt the band pestered him with questions. How far was it? How long would it take? Were they nearly there?

He could only answer them vaguely.

Then Willy spoke up. "You've got your bugle, Michael! I've got my drum. You play! The others can sing! Here, Velma, you hold this. Don't lose it."

Michael saw that Willy was handing Margot a small black case with a handle. The case was Mr. Budd's typewriter!

"Willy, where did you get that?"

"I stumbled over it, Michael, at the foot of the ladder. It must have fallen over the edge when Mr. Budd left it in the shaft house. I'm keeping it for him. He'd feel pretty bad if anything happened to his typewriter. I guess it can be fixed."

Willy stopped pumping the flashlight to rest his hand. Darkness was all around them.

The typewriter the Mountie wanted! Willy had found it. Michael knew then they had an added reason for getting out of the mine. Somehow, he must get them out safely.

The more he thought of the typewriter, the surer he

THE MYSTERY OF THE PIPER'S GHOST

was that Mr. Budd had not put the case containing it too close to the shaft. He had thrown it down the shaft. Mr. Budd knew now that the Mountie wanted it. This was his way of hiding the typewriter forever.

Another thought came to Michael. When Mr. Budd had thrown the rug on the roof, and stooped down out of sight, he could have been lighting a match. Mr. Budd wanted to burn down the shaft house. Why? So he wouldn't have to open the mine! So he could make off with the villagers' savings. The idea shocked him, but rang true.

"Play, Michael! Play!" Willy's voice cut urgently through the gloom. Very softly he started a few bars of "Hail! Hail! The Gang's All Here!"

Then he handed Velma the flashlight, and gave the order to march. Willy played a gentle rat-a-tat-tatta-tat-tat! They began to sing; singing gave them new courage. His own was almost gone. Zeb was the only one in the village who knew the secret of the other opening to the mine and Zeb had gone away. He and his pack had vanished into the deep woods. They were lost!

The next time they rested, Michael knew that Willy's hands were busy. He seemed to be using his knife. But he was surprised when Willy presented Stephen with a rude crutch made of planking, and bound at the top with a handkerchief. He had picked up the wood along the way.

The march started again, with Stephen hobbling on his own.

Allwyn got the flashlight. He was pumping it vigorously, but the beam wavered, and Michael guessed his
arm was beginning to tire.

"My mouth's dry." Allwyn's voice was a whine. "I've
got to have a drink of water."

Michael's own throat was parched. He remembered
they had neither food nor water with them. They had
brought food to the picnic, but there was to be a general
sharing. The food packages had been dropped beside the
women.

The plan had been to fill their canteens at the brook
which crossed Zeb's place. But none of them had done so.
Allwyn and Stephen and Willy and himself had canteens,
but they were empty. Margot had left hers at the shaft
mouth.

Michael called a halt to consider what they should do.
Stephen tried to use his injured foot. He collapsed in a
faint. The need for water had become immediate.

Michael ordered quiet. Everyone listened. He had
heard the drip, drip of water the night he had visited the
mine with Zeb. Now he heard nothing. Perhaps they had
passed the opening. Horror seized him. Would they have
to turn back? There was only one flashlight.

Allwyn became unexpectedly helpful. "I heard water
at the last opening," he announced. "Look, Michael! I've
got a salmon line in my pocket. You can hold the reel and
pay out the line. Two of us will go. That way we can get
back. I'll take the flashlight. We'll fill all the canteens."

Michael let him take the light reluctantly. He wished

Margot had offered to go with him. But it was Velma who went. Margot had courage. He wondered why she didn't go.

Allwyn and Velma left. For a minute or two the only sound in the mine was the click of the salmon line being payed out by the reel. They followed the faint glimmer of the flashlight. Then Allwyn and Velma turned a corner, and the light disappeared. Only the steady unreeling of the line told him they were still in touch.

Margot moved closer in the darkness. "Michael!" she whispered.

"Yes, Margot!"

"I'm sorry, Michael, for the nasty things I said to you."

"That's all right, Margot," he answered. He wondered if she would ever hurt him again. Her taunts seemed so unimportant now.

"Michael, you think we'll get out all right?"

Willy answered for him. "Michael will get us out, Margot. He knows the way."

Michael had an odd feeling inside. Willy believed in him.

He was glad when they began to talk together. He had time to think. He thought he knew the way to the far side of the mine. It was the turn off into the last gallery that worried him. Zeb had been a little vague about that. It was on the part of the blueprint that was missing. But he did remember Zeb saying that last day, "The last gallery, Michael, runs downhill." The remark was one of the things that made him so sure Zeb had found the way out of the mine.

Presently he gave a little tug on the line. A long time seemed to have passed since they had left. He hoped Allwyn hadn't dropped the flashlight into the pond. Without light, they were lost.

An answering tug and a faint glimmer of light in the gloom down the gallery reassured him. They were coming back! A load fell from Michael.

The water revived Stephen, and refreshed them all. The weary march started once more.

He wondered how long it would be until they were missed. Would the villagers start digging down the shaft? Had he been right in leading them away from it?

The air was getting colder. Did that mean anything? Velma was shivering, and he made her take his coat. Willy put his around Margot. Then Michael sensed that Velma was limping.

"I lost my sandals, Michael," she told him, "coming down the first ladder!" There was a quiver of pain in her voice. He took off his own shoes and made her put them on. The floor of the mine was of jagged rock. When they started on again, he knew what she had suffered. His own feet were cut. It became agony to walk. He wondered how Velma, a girl, had walked barefoot so far. And she had gone for the water, too. But something she said was unexpectedly helpful.

"We've been following a rail track for a long time, Michael. I put one foot on the rail. It helped."

He had known the rails were there, but he had not thought what the tracks meant. Was it reasonable to suppose that the tracks led out of the mine? He decided it

135

was. When he came to the dividing of the way, he would follow the rails.

Velma began to sing "Men of Harlech." Singing kept up their courage.

Cy Sullivan's Band was marching bravely forward through the dark underground passages of old Kejimaku-jee.

But only Michael knew the deep, dark waters that lay ahead.

15.   OVER THE AIRWAYS OF B.B.C.

FOR some time Ma Lovey had been thinking of making a visit. She was going to see Zeb for herself. By all accounts, he didn't welcome strangers, but she felt it was time she knew something of this friend of Michael's. After the first excitement of the bugle wore off, she was sure Michael would go back to Zeb's.

Today, as she climbed the hill to join the women at the picnic tables, it·occurred to her this was as good a time as any to call on Zeb.

When she reached the cabin, Zeb wasn't home. The padlock on the cabin door suggested that he had gone away, and the absence of the crow and the ducks told her he wasn't coming back immediately.

Ma wondered if Michael knew. Since he had had the bugle, he had said almost nothing about Zeb.

She was turning away when a voice stopped her. "Did you wish something, ma'am?" Zeb was standing in the pathway behind her. It was the first time Ma Lovey had seen Zeb close. She understood at once why Michael had enjoyed coming here. There was something likable about Zeb.

Ma held out her hand.

"I just wanted to make a friendly call," she explained. "I'm Ma Lovey, Michael's foster mother. I came to thank you for your kindness to him. I—I was afraid you had gone away."

"I had," Zeb smiled. His voice sounded friendly. "I just came back for my pipe! But since you're here, won't you come in and rest a moment!" Zeb began unlocking the door. "I'm all packed up, as you can see." He pulled up the cushionless rocker for Ma to sit in.

Ma thanked him and sat down. The forgotten pipe lay on the table. Zeb smiled as he retrieved it.

"Michael talked of you so much, Zeb, I had to come."

"That was brave of you, Ma."

"But I knew about Beelzebub," Ma confessed.

"Someone's been talking," Zeb answered. They both laughed. "But since you're here, Ma Lovey, I'd like to take this opportunity to tell you who I am."

Ma was surprised. Zeb wanted to be friendly. The stories she had heard about him couldn't be true. Zeb was opening his billfold. He handed her a folded paper. Ma opened it curiously.

"An honorable discharge from the Royal Canadian Engineers," she read. "With disability to one Zebediah MacHarg! Why you, you must be a relative of the MacHarg who owned the mine."

"Yes, ma'am, his nephew. I was in the war. Got dumped into the drink off England. Pneumonia followed. I had to rest up. Remembered the cabin. Recently, Uncle wanted me to keep an eye on the mine. He wasn't too sure what his partners were up to. They were renting out the rights."

Ma nodded. "I'm afraid, Zeb, his fears were justified."

"You bet they were. Those old mazards—" Zeb stopped. He looked uncomfortable. "Sorry, ma'am. The word slipped out."

Ma laughed. She handed him back his papers. "Thank you for telling me about yourself, Zeb. I like to know Michael's friends."

Zeb leaned forward. "He's a fine lad, Ma. You've done a grand job bringing him up. Don't let anybody tell you differently."

Ma thanked him. "Sometimes, Zeb, I haven't felt too sure of what I've done. But he *is* a fine boy."

"Believe me, Ma," Zeb began. He never finished the sentence. Distant shouts and cries broke in.

"Something has happened," Ma said and rushed to the doorway. A great pall of smoke was rising above the trees.

"It's the old shaft house," Zeb cried. "It's—it's on fire!"

Ma started down the trail. Zeb followed.

At a turn of the road they met the Mountie and Scout racing up the hill. "Zeb! Thank goodness you're still here!"

the Mountie greeted them. "The shaft house is on fire. And Michael and Margot and the rest are below."

At Michael's name Ma uttered a cry and dashed down the hill.

"Michael in the mine!" Zeb was startled. "He promised me—"

"I know! But something took him down. Come!"

When they reached the shaft house it was a blazing torch. Zeb pushed his way through the crowd of frightened men and women. He went right up to the blistering heat of it. The walls were gone. The roof had fallen. Only the rafters were left and they were burning. You could look right through them to the trees beyond.

Zeb came back white-faced. "It would take hours to hack a way down," he said.

"He's a coward!" Margot's mother shouted. She was crazy with fear.

"Quiet, woman!" The Mountie ordered. "Zeb knows the mine." He turned to Zeb. "Can we get in by the other entrance, Zeb?"

"Possibly," Zeb answered. He strode off through the trees.

A handful of the villagers followed him. Most of them stayed by the shaft house, fighting the fire that threatened to spread up the hill. Zeb led the way through bog and bramble. He didn't wait for trails. When he stopped they were beside the Piper's Pool.

"Wait here!" he commanded them, and strode into the woods on the far side. When he came out, he had on the Piper's suit.

"Zeb was the Piper!" Everyone gasped. Zeb didn't wait to explain. He waded into the Pool, ducked under and disappeared! A second gasp broke from the amazed group.

The Mountie reassured them. "It's all right!" he said. "Zeb won't drown in that old army frogman's suit."

The minutes passed. It seemed as if Zeb had indeed disappeared. The Mountie strode down to the Pool, as if he, too, were going to wade in, as he was. But just then Zeb's head rose out of the surface of the Pool. He came ashore, slipping off his mask.

"The entrance to the tunnel into the mine is under the waters of the Pool," he informed them, "and it's blocked." He threw back his head and scanned the cliff above them. "Whoever set fire to the shaft house first let loose a boulder from the top of the cliff." They could see the scar where the boulder had come crashing down.

"Then let's go in. Blast it open!" Ed Moorhans pushed forward. "My son Allwyn is in there."

"No!" Zeb's voice rang out. "There is still an opening big enough for a boy or girl to crawl through. Blasting might start the bluff coming down. Might disturb the old shoring inside the mine. Could cut off their escape altogether. Michael knows there's an opening here, somewhere. He'll bring them here. The water's the chief trouble. Got to think of a way to get them through it. The top of the entrance is under water. For the first few yards inside it's over a man's head."

Zeb was plainly worried. The Mountie's face was sober.

Many disagreed with Zeb. They were all for blasting

and going in, but the Mountie backed Zeb. "Zeb is an engineer," he said firmly. "He's familiar with the mine. He knows."

"If they are not out by nine o'clock tonight," Zeb said, "we'll take a chance. We'll blast and go in. But—let's wait now."

The village of Portopeake started its vigil.

"Zeb," the Mountie said, "could we drain the Pool?"

Zeb started. "It's an idea, Captain. The Pool is caused by a spring which broke out of the mine. You can't dam it from this side but—we might lower the height of the water. If we could get it only a few inches below the top of the entrance, it would help. Michael doesn't know it's under water. I wish I'd told him. I've been worrying about how they'd know it was the entrance, if all they could see was dark water. But if across the water they could catch a gleam of daylight, they'd know."

"And we could talk to them, direct them," said the Mountie.

"Yes." Zeb's tone was eager. "It would help to get them out."

The Mountie ordered pumps to work. Very soon their hurried panting could be heard all over the hill. Could they get the water out of the Pool faster than it was running in? As soon as he saw the pumps were working, Zeb made for the vent on top of the hill.

News of the disaster had got around. A small crowd followed him over the hill.

"You can't talk down the vent," Zeb warned them. "Your voice could reverberate into a roar. It might terrify them, turn them back. Also, it could start some of the loose rock falling. But if we listen we may catch the sound of a voice. They ought to reach here about five o'clock—if the way thus far is clear."

The crowd began its listening watch. One! Two! Three! Four! Five! Five-thirty!

Ma's face was white. Zeb was grim. Joe Westerley paced the ground and Ed Moorhans stormed.

At last the Mountie said quietly, "Any chance that you were wrong, Zeb? Want to start blasting?"

Zeb shook his head. Presently he said, "I've just thought of something. One or more may be injured. That would slow them up. We'll wait."

They waited!

Six o'clock!

Six-thirty!

Velma's mother was sobbing aloud. Joe Westerley looked ready to break. Ma bit her trembling lips. Mr. Glendinning moved back and forth among them, speaking words of comfort. Father Stephen, too, from Cameronia, was there boosting their courage. Many had gathered from the neighboring villages. The crowd grew larger.

A band of boys and girls, lost in a mine. It was a human story. Here and there a reporter was making notes.

"It's like the old days," someone said. "Kejimakujee has known disaster before."

Then, movement around the vent, a warning gesture for silence.

Faintly to those nearby, borne up from the earth, came

a few scattered strains of song, rising and dying. "Hail! Hail! The Gang's All Here!"

Then the clear sweet note of a bugle and a faint rat-a-tat-tatta-tat-tat of a midget drum.

"Bless the Lord! That's my Willy!" shouted Auntie Sammy, and Ma wondered whether the bugle was Michael's.

Then silence again.

Zeb got up abruptly. He was frowning.

"Something wrong, Zeb?" the Mountie questioned, as he drew away from the crowd.

"That drum!" Zeb murmured. "The beat of it—the mine's old—the shoring is rotten—it may be dangerous!"

"But it's only a midget drum!" the Mountie answered.

Then Ma's voice crying, "Are there more vents, Zeb? Can we hear them again?"

"There is one more," Zeb told her. "They should reach it by eight o'clock."

The crowd shifted once more, over the hill.

Meanwhile, CHNS in Halifax had started broadcasting the story. Ma, sitting by the vent, caught the voice on Lennie's radio. "A young lad, at this very moment, is leading his pals through the dark galleries of an abandoned mine in Portopeake, Nova Scotia. They are trouping through the darkness, far below the surface of the earth. A young orphan, Michael Cunningham, is leading."

Ma had her ear to the vent. But only silence greeted her. Her attention went back to the radio.

"The story is being rebroadcast over the B.B.C.," the voice went on. Countless people in many and distant lands were listening! All over the world, the tragic story of parentless Michael, and his brave fight to save his comrades, was being retold. Wherever the B.B.C. reached its millions of listeners, the question was being asked, Would Michael Cunningham be able to lead his comrades out?

Ma Lovey lifted her face to the sky. The world had become one family, she thought.

Eight o'clock! The waiting crowd around Ma Lovey and Zeb and the Mountie hushed into silence.

Now it was Colin and Lennie who first caught the voices: Velma's high soprano, Margot's faltering alto, Allwyn's tenor, whipping up their courage with faltering notes of song. But the rhythm of the bugle and the little drum were missing. What did it mean?

"They're coming! They're coming!" the cry went up from the waiting hillside and was caught up by the listening mikes.

Once more the sound from the depths passed on. Was the way ahead of the little band clear? Nobody knew. There was nothing to do but wait and keep the pumps going.

They all moved on to the Pool.

At last the pumps were making progress! A murmur rose and spread all over the hill. The top of the entrance to the tunnel could be seen.

Men and women milled about the quiet water. The tiny opening in the rock about the surface of the Pool was growing larger.

The hands of the clock were nearing ten-thirty. Zeb

and the Mountie appeared at the Pool. It was the signal to stand by for the end.

But only Zeb and the Mountie realized that the hardest part was yet to come. Would the waters get low enough for them to send in a small float?

Zeb had set the time for nine o'clock! But they had been late at the first vent. He was giving them extra time.

Would Michael remember that the road went downhill, and would he follow the rails at the last turnoff? The questions raced through Zeb's brain.

Now and then in the crowd one caught ugly murmurs. The fire was set! The men who did this should be imprisoned!

But Zeb and Ma Lovey and the Mountie were thinking only of Michael and his band.

At last Zeb got up stiffly from the rock on which he had been sitting. He and the Mountie and Scout got into a boat that had been brought to the Pool. Zeb had on the Piper's suit.

The pumps stopped! The sudden silence was awesome. The Mountie stood up in the boat and he addressed the crowd.

"Fathers and mothers! Men and women! From now on we are requesting absolute silence. We must hear what the children have to say. We have to find out what condition they are in. We suspect that at least one of them is injured."

Ma Lovey's lips moved. She had been murmuring prayers for Michael's safety all afternoon.

The boat moved out over the Pool. Behind it was a

145

rubber tire into which had been fitted a floor of canvas sailcloth. The boat reached the rock opening. Zeb and the Mountie could be seen leaning far over the side. They examined the hole in the rock that was gradually appearing over the water of the Pool.

The Mountie leaned far into the opening. Did he hear anything? Were they actually there at last, behind that solid wall of rock, across a dark stretch of water?

Then over the torchlit surface of the Pool, in the midst of a great silence, they caught the Mountie's clear ringing tones.

"Michael! Michael! Can you hear me?"

Tensely the crowd waited.

And then—Zeb turned! He waved his arms. Tears were coursing down his cheeks! The crowd knew. Michael had answered!

A sudden, wild "hurrah!" burst from the crowd. Nothing could have stopped it. They knew. The rescuers had made contact! Could they get the band out?

Silence again—and waiting!

The Mountie was pushing Scout into the opening. The big dog could just make it. Tied to his collar was the little rubber float. It, too, just managed to squeeze through.

Two minutes! Three minutes! Five minutes passed! To Ma Lovey the time seemed years.

And then the Mountie could be seen reaching into the opening. The crowd held its breath. A moment later they saw him pull back, his arms full of a burden. A small form was passed to Zeb.

Again cheers broke from the crowd but were quickly

146

stifled. Stephen, the injured one, was saved! Men waded down into the quarry up to their shoulders to pass him ashore.

Margot's turn was next; Joe Westerley caught her up and placed her in her mother's arms. There wasn't a dry eye in the crowd. And still the Mountie and Zeb in the boat, before the opening, reached in for the precious burden Scout was ferrying back and forth to safety. Velma, Allwyn, Willy—five of the six were safe!

"I wanted to be last," Willy's voice rang out in the stillness, "but Michael wouldn't let me!" Auntie Sammy smothered him in her arms.

Ma Lovey trembled. She was proud that Michael waited till the last. But she was desperately afraid. Suppose a rock fell, closing up the opening, or the waters of the Pool welled up again, now the pumps had stopped!

But now at last it was Michael's turn. But first they saw a small square satchel being pushed through the opening. What was it? Why was Michael saving it before he saved himself? Then Michael was seen. He was pushing Scout through. Cheers greeted him. Cy Sullivan's entire band was safe!

Michael's first words were for Ma. Then he turned to Zeb and the Mountie. "We have it," he cried excitedly, patting the small tin box. "Mr. Budd's typewriter! Willy found it! He carried it most of the way."

"Michael!" Captain MacKay's voice was full of satisfaction. "That does it! We'll catch the beggars now."

Then Ma Lovey's wail broke the night. "Michael's hurt! His feet are bleeding!"

16.   MICHAEL MAKES GOOD

MICHAEL sat on the steps of Ma Lovey's front porch. His feet still hurt him when he walked. But his hands, blistered by the slide down the ladder, had healed.

It was good to sit in the sun and watch Colin's cutter patterning the still water of the cove with fantail ripples. Everything left its mark, the Mountie had said. He still didn't like to think of the dark hours in the mine. He had been so sure he would never see the homing lobster fleet again.

It was good to feel in his pocket the yellow slip the Mountie had handed Ma Lovey the day after the accident.

Michael knew each word of the radiogram by heart. "Heard broadcast. Consult British Intelligence on Mike Cunningham of Dornoch, Scotland. Disappeared en route to England, with wife and American-born child. Thought shot down, using assumed name for security reasons. A brave buddy."

He knew now that his parents had not abandoned him. They had been taking him to England. And in those last terrible moments on the plane, their one thought had been that he should know he belonged to them. The couple who had perished on the plane were his own parents. They had been traveling under another name. Later correspondence proved the point. Major Mike Cunningham had had a distinguished record! Someday, Ma promised, they would go to Dornoch and hunt up his father's and mother's people.

Ma Lovey and Elmira McCabe came out of the house.

Elmira stopped beside him. "That was a brave thing you did, Michael," Elmira said. "I hope you never go back o your wild ways."

"No, ma'am!" Michael answered meekly. Elmira, he thought, was like unripe gooseberries, hard to take. But it was good to have people liking him again.

After Elmira left, Ma dropped down on the step beside him.

The Mountie was coming up the path with Zeb! The Mountie had been to Halifax. He would tell them about Mr. Budd and Mr. Harte. Word was they had been caught. Dancing along beside them was Willy with Desdemona on his shoulder. Desdemona was shouting, " 'Ello! 'Ello! I'm Auntie Sammy's boy!"

Scout trotted on ahead. He buried his shaggy head in Michael's lap. His big brown eyes seemed to be saying, "We've been through things together. We're pals now." The Mountie had his creel. They must be going fishing, Michael thought. He wished he could go with them.

"What happened in Halifax, Captain MacKay?" Ma demanded. "Did you really catch Mr. Budd and Mr. Harte trying to get away with all the money the Portopeake people had invested in the mine?"

"We did, Ma, thanks to Michael and Willy here. Those

two won't rob anyone else with their schemes for a long time."

Willy said, "I'm sorry Mr. Budd had to be bad. He was awful good to Auntie Sammy and me."

"Did the typewriter really help, Captain MacKay?" Michael asked.

"Indeed it did, Michael!" the Mountie answered. "You see, we felt sure the letter from the experts saying the mine was full of gold was a fake. When we wrote to the company they said they had never written the letter, although it was on their letterhead."

"You mean they stole the paper to make it look official?" Ma asked.

"Yes, Ma," the Mountie answered. "That's exactly what happened. But you know, Michael, I told you everything left a trail, even machines?"

Michael nodded.

"Well, when you brought me Mr. Budd's machine out of the mine, even though it wouldn't write any more, I could tell that the fake letter had been written on it. Every single *g*, under the microscope, in the letter had a broken tail. The type bar for *g* on the machine had a broken-tailed *g*, too. And every *o* in the letter—it's written with the third finger under the touch system—was lighter than any other character, all through the letter. We found Mr. Budd had an injured third finger on his right hand. We knew then the engineer's letter had been written on his machine and must be a fraud. It had gone through the mails, having been put in the post office in Halifax. We had him there."

"And the money?" demanded Ma.

"It was still in the car, Ma. Mr. Budd very cleverly had had a secret compartment built into the underside of the driver's seat."

"It was a new one on me!" Captain MacKay laughed. "Actually, I was looking for a larger space. Mr. Budd's typewriter was Swiss, and smaller than any I had ever seen. The case wasn't much bigger than a woman's handbag."

Michael thought happily, the people of Portopeake will all get back their hard-earned savings. Then he remembered something.

"Willy and I saw him put the rug on the roof, Captain MacKay," he said. Captain MacKay looked surprised.

"Michael won't have to go into court, will he?" Ma asked quickly.

"No," the Mountie seemed sure of that. "I don't think that will be necessary, although it is nice to have a witness to it. But we have other proof of his having set fire to the shaft house. While Zeb and I were examining the roof where the fire started, Desdemona went pecking into the ashes, near where the fire was set. She came up with something bright. We thought it was a bit of glass at first. Then we discovered it was the diamond from Mr. Budd's ring!"

"That Desdemona is a mighty smart bird, Captain," Willy cried. And Michael thought, Zeb was right to give her to Willy. Willy has been teaching her things.

Zeb said, "We know she's smart, Willy. Funny thing was, when we caught Budd the stone in his ring was missing from the setting. And when we returned stone and ring to the jeweler whose name was inside, he identified the diamond as one of their cutting. He also had a record of selling it to Mr. Budd."

Ma said, "Think of a bird, a crow, being a detective!" The idea amused them all.

"Well," the Mountie said, "I imagine that just about winds up the case of the people of Portopeake versus Budd and Harte. Come, Scout! Why you old coot, I believe Michael is weaning you away from me. Maybe—maybe he's just routing for a new recruit. Maybe there will be a place for you on the force, Michael, only—you'll have to get your education first. There's an awful lot a Mountie has to know."

"And it's just about the finest calling in the world!" Zeb reminded them.

The Mountie looked pleased. "Thank you, Zeb. Thank you very much. Well, I must be on my way."

But the Mountie didn't go. Instead, he made a little speech. "The Department, Michael, is very grateful for your help in catching two rather dreadful rogues! They wish to make you a small gift."

The Mountie put his hand in his creel. A soft bundle of squirming fur dropped into Michael's lap. Michael clutched the dog to him, and a cold nose snuggled into his neck.

"His name," the Mountie said softly, "is Whirlwind Scout."

A dog! A dog of his own. Michael couldn't speak. With a dog of his own he'd never be lonely!

Willy answered for him. "Michael and me, Captain MacKay, we'll teach him his manners."

The Mountie laughed. "Then that's settled. Tell you a secret, Michael. Scout's his father." Scout, Michael noticed, seemed as interested in the puppy as he was himself. But he went when the Mountie called him.

"Give you a lift home, Willy?" Willy went proudly off with the Mountie. Ma walked to the road with them.

Michael and Zeb were left alone.

"Zeb!" Michael said.

"Yes, minikin!" The old name sounded good to Michael.

"In the paper, Zeb, it said I was brave, but I wasn't. I was awfully scared. I didn't want to go down into the mine. I almost didn't."

"Is that so, minikin?" Zeb didn't sound at all shocked. "But you see, minikin, you did go, and that is what mattered. If you hadn't gone down, Willy wouldn't have followed you, and then we might never have gotten the proof we needed that Mr. Budd was operating outside the law. The people of Portopeake would have lost their money."

"I guess it's good I made myself go down," Michael said, his nose buried in the puppy's soft fur.

"I guess it was, Michael. Without you and Willy, the others would have been lost."

Down in the cove a boat was throwing out bait. The gulls were like a cloud of snowflakes about it. Their bodies glistened white against the gray sea. They were circling quietly. This was their home.

"Zeb!"

"Something more on your mind, minikin?"

"I was on the high rocks one night, above the Pool, and you came out of the woods in your frogman's suit. You stopped and looked up when a pebble fell."

Zeb started. "So it was you, Michael. I thought it was Budd spying on me. And you thought I was the Piper. Is that why you stayed away so long?"

Michael nodded.

"I'm glad you told me, Michael. I was the Piper, but only for that night or two. You remember you told me you had seen the Piper in the mine? The Mountie and I knew someone was planting gold in the mine to make the people of Portopeake think there was gold there. We were trying to catch him. We had a signal between us, the moosecall."

Michael was amazed. He knew Zeb was a caller, but he had never thought of that.

"Well," Zeb continued, "that speech of yours was what first led me to consider there might be some connection between the Pool and the mine. I decided then that was how he was getting into the mine, without our seeing him go in and out. It gave me the clue to where the other exit must be. No wonder I had never found it. It was under the waters of the Pool. Perhaps if I'd had the full blueprint, it might have shown it coming out in the quarry, now a pool."

"Zeb, who was the Piper?"

Zeb didn't answer immediately. "I'll tell you, Michael," he said at last. "And then you must forget you ever knew. The Piper was Joe Westerley!"

"Oh, no, Zeb. He couldn't be!" Michael cried. Joe had been so good to the young crowd. He always welcomed them in his boat shop. Then Michael remembered the short, stocky figure of the Piper, the trudging walk. "Oh, Zeb! What will they do to him?"

"Nothing, I hope, Michael! You see, Joe had seen the engineer's report. Joe didn't know it was a fake. Budd persuaded him there was plenty of gold in the mine but it couldn't be mined without men and machinery, and that would cost money. But everyone who put money into the mine would eventually be rich. In putting in the false veins of gold to convince the people of Portopeake the gold was there to see, Joe thought he was just persuading the villagers to put their money in a good thing. Joe's so simple and honest himself, he believed he was doing the right thing."

Long after Zeb had left, Michael sat on the step, Whirlwind's warm body snuggling in his arms.

Ma, coming up the path, joined him. She sat down close beside him. "I used to wonder, Michael," she said, "why you were saved when all the others were lost in the plane crack-up, and why you came to us on Christmas Eve. But I think I know now—the day was coming when the children of Portopeake would need you. Oh, Michael, I'm so proud of you!" Ma Lovey's arm stole around him.

And Michael thought his parents had given him an honored name, but Ma Lovey had shown him how to deserve it. And she would never, never send him away. He was sure of that now.

THE GOLDEN
GARDEN GUIDE

A PRACTICAL HANDBOOK
OF GARDENING
AND OUTDOOR LIVING

Edited by
JOHN STROHM

PREPARED IN COOPERATION
WITH FORD MOTOR COMPANY

GOLDEN PRESS NEW YORK

Contents

Art Direction by Ole Risom • Cover by Ned Seidler
Illustrations by William Sayles and Peter Spier

Second Printing, 1961

© Copyright 1960 by Ford Motor Co., Golden Press, and Artists and Writers Press, Inc.
All rights reserved. Printed in U.S.A. by Western Printing and Lithographing Co.

Introduction

Though gardening is man's oldest avocation, it has never been as interesting, exciting, satisfying, and rewarding as today. That holds true whether you're the chief gardener of a lone window box or have space for thousands of blossoms, shrubs, and trees.

Scientists are at work as never before to make your garden better. Flower hybridizers are making spectacular new blooms—bigger, hardier, longer-lasting, and in more colors. Even atomic scientists have entered the picture. They are exposing seeds, plants, and trees to the bombardment of deadly but useful rays that cause mutations—changes that may mean new and useful varieties for your garden.

All this attention to gardening has resulted in a flood of new techniques, facts, equipment, and ideas. The aim of this handbook is to give such up-to-the-minute information. And the fundamentals of gardening are here, too—how to plant, fertilize, prune, and water plants for best results. There are also many ideas on outdoor living and improving your grounds, both closely linked to gardening.

This garden guide does not pretend to tell the complete gardening story. It *does* attempt to give those facts that will be most useful and interesting to you. We hope you like it.

JOHN STROHM, Editor
Woodstock, Illinois

Planning Your Grounds

A landscape plan for your grounds is the key to beauty, comfort, and convenience. And it can save you time and money by preventing costly mistakes, such as planting a tree where you later want a walk or flower border. Planning is so important that some people hire professional landscape architects to do it for them. Some nurseries also offer landscape plans and suggestions as a service with their plant materials.

But it's not too hard to draw up your own plan. Keep your eyes and ears open for new ideas and use what you like. The result will be something you can be really proud of, for it will be your own creation.

Put Your Plan on Paper.

Your first move is to measure the yard and draw a scale map showing what you have. You can let 1 inch equal 20 feet or use any other scale that allows the map of your grounds to fit on the paper.

Paper ruled in squares makes drawing to scale easier. The squares can be used as the scale, say one square equaling 2 feet, and the lines can serve as guides in drawing square and rectangular areas.

In drawing your map, follow these steps:

STEP 1: Draw the outside boundaries to scale. For a city or suburban lot, use property lines; for rural acreage, use fences or natural dividing lines between yard and field.

STEP 2: Draw in the house and other buildings. Be sure to show windows and doors, for these are a guide to locating new shrubs and plantings.

STEP 3: If you are improving an old landscape, add trees, shrubs, and walks already there.

You're now ready to decide what old features should be removed for the best over-all plan and what new features should be added.

Aim for These Goals.

Think in broad terms of what you want from your property. Keep the following goals in mind:

MORE BEAUTY. A goal of landscaping is to make house and grounds look as if they belong together. A well-landscaped place presents a balanced, attractive picture from any direction.

MORE COMFORT. A good plan also considers the comfort you get from shade in the right places, privacy fenced in, but cool breezes not fenced out.

EASIER UPKEEP. You may think landscaping means a lot of extra work—digging, pruning, and clipping. Not so. Good planning can mean your yard is easier to keep.

For example, a well-landscaped lawn has no scattered plantings. Shrubs and flowers are at the edges, making it easier to mow. You can also select shrubs or ground covers that take little pruning and care.

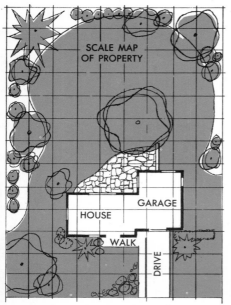

SCALE MAP OF PROPERTY

GARAGE

HOUSE

WALK

DRIVE

MORE ENJOYMENT. Your family's favorite home recreations or hobbies can be planned into the landscape. You may want a patio for entertaining or a spot to grow roses. If your children are small, they may want a sandbox or swings. If they are teenagers, they may want a paved outdoor area for dancing and entertaining.

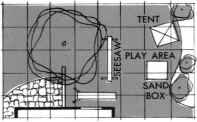

ADDED VALUE. If you should decide to move—and many people do —the money and work you have invested in landscaping isn't lost. Real estate salesmen will tell you good landscaping increases the value of your property and helps you sell it faster. As plants grow, they add to your investment.

Plan the Key Areas.
To make the most of your space, coordinate your key outdoor areas with indoor areas. Keep in mind your needs, your hobbies, and the way you like to entertain.

APPROACH AREA. A front yard need not be large. Its main purpose is to create an attractive view of your home. Usually a simple lawn with limited planting does the best job.

OUTDOOR LIVING AREA. This is the place for a family picnic, entertaining friends, or just a spot to sit and relax. Since privacy will make this area more enjoyable, screen it with shrubbery and fences. Allow plenty of space so the area doesn't seem crowded. Include a patio, perhaps a pool, and the flowers you like best.

You'll make more use of the outdoor living area if it is connected closely to the living area of the house. A door to the patio, for example, makes it easier to have meals outdoors. A screened porch gives a feeling of closeness between house and outdoor living room.

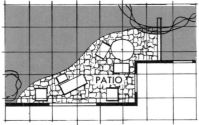

WORK AREA. This area may be quite small, but should be convenient to the kitchen and garage. It can be used for clotheslines, vegetable garden, hobbies, doing odd jobs, etc.

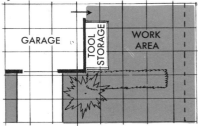

Plant to Make a Picture.

Landscaping is much like painting a three-dimensional picture. By using different shapes and colors of trees, shrubs, and flowers, you create an attractive view of your home. Here are some elements in the design of good pictures, as applied to landscaping your grounds. Many variations of these elements are possible.

A GOOD FRAME separates your house from the surroundings beyond your yard. Trees at the lot line can provide that frame.

AN ATTRACTIVE FOREGROUND of grass, trees, and shrubs creates a pleasant setting for your home.

A BACKGROUND of large trees softens the silhouette of the house against the sky.

WELL-PLACED ACCENTS draw attention to important parts of your home, such as the front door.

THE SLOPE OF YOUR PLANTINGS should draw the eye to the center of the house or to the front entrance.

Put these elements together and you will have a well-balanced picture.

One common mistake to avoid is that of not considering how the growth of plants will affect your picture. Some plants grow so fast they soon hide your home. You have to be especially careful of this if your house is small.

Paint with Flowers. The colors of your landscape picture are provided by flowers available in shades of red, yellow, blue, orange, pink, violet, green, gray, and white. Use these flowers as an artist uses his paints, making them accent, frame, or blend with your home, trees, and other features. Use them inside your home, too. Some pointers to guide you:

RED usually is the strongest color and is most pleasing when softened with yellows and blues. For touches of red, plant celosia, dahlia, salvia, or zinnia.

YELLOW AND WHITE combine to give a cool effect and show up well on dark days or in dark corners of a yard. Common yellow flowers are marigold, savitalia, zinnia, calendula, snapdragon, sunflower, nasturtium, hollyhock. White flowers include snapdragon, candytuft, alyssum, aster, gypsophila, phlox, verbena, petunia.

BLUE will blend with any other color. (It is lovely in flower arrangements in silver or pewter containers.) Most popular blues are salvia, forget-me-not, nemophila, pansy, scabiosa, primrose, bachelor button, larkspur, ageratum.

By experimenting you can achieve striking color effects. If the color combinations are pleasant to you, that's what really matters. If you doubt that colors will blend, separate them with white flowers.

Before You Buy or Build.

Anyone who is buying or building a home is in an ideal position to plan his grounds so that everything is just as he wants it. Here are some things to think about.

THE LOT. Corner lots are usually larger than other lots, but may not be as useful. Since building codes generally require the house to be a certain distance from the street, you have a large front and side yard, but little space in back for privacy.

Elevation is important. High lots afford good views, adequate drainage and air circulation. Low lots are often damp, hot in summer, and subject to early frost.

Trees on a lot are priceless—if they aren't located right where the house should go.

HOUSE AND GARAGE. The location of your house and garage limits what you can do in the rest of your yard. Placing the house and garage near the front of a property allows more space in the rear for outdoor living and gardening.

DRIVEWAY AND PARKING. If you entertain a lot, a parking area for guests is handy, but it can eat up valuable space. One possibility is an extra-wide driveway, with room for one or two cars to park.

If you are short of space, consider a "landing strip" of paving alongside a narrow drive. It solves the problem of stepping from the car into wet grass or mud.

STREET

SIDEWALK

DRIVE

CANNOT BUILD HERE

GARAGE

LIMITED AREA FOR OUTDOOR LIVING

HOUSE

STREET

BEWARE THE CORNER LOT

HIGH LOT HAS GOOD VIEW AND DRAINAGE

Front lawn too large and broken up

Long drive wastes space, is costly

Turnaround uses valuable space

Limited space for outdoor living

Garage location is inconvenient, wastes outdoor-living space

POOR PLAN

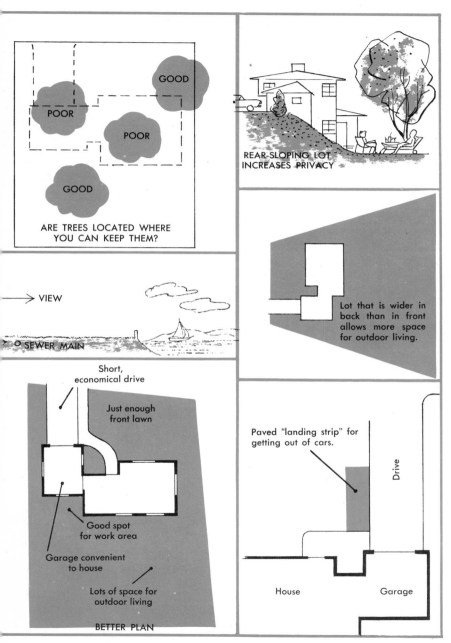

GOOD

POOR

POOR

GOOD

ARE TREES LOCATED WHERE
YOU CAN KEEP THEM?

REAR-SLOPING LOT
INCREASES PRIVACY

→ VIEW

O SEWER MAIN

Lot that is wider in
back than in front
allows more space
for outdoor living.

Short,
economical drive

Just enough
front lawn

Good spot
for work area

Garage convenient
to house

Lots of space for
outdoor living

BETTER PLAN

Paved "landing strip" for
getting out of cars.

Drive

House

Garage

Walks, Steps, and Walls.

These are meant to serve a practical purpose. So, in planning them, think of that first. Then consider how they can be made an attractive part of your grounds.

WALKS should be planned to tie your use areas together and serve your way of living and entertaining. Think hard about where you'll have the most foot traffic.

There are many beautiful materials you can choose to build a walk: colorful bricks, wood blocks, stepping stones, colored concrete, tanbark, etc. Using the same paving you have on your patio or drive gives a look of unity to your yard.

A RETAINING WALL is the best means to build up level areas for a lawn or patio in a sloping yard. A wall has many advantages over earth terracing. A steep slope of grass is hard to get started, hard to mow, and often washes out during a rain. Also, a wall adds color and variation to the design of your yard.

A wall can be built with stone, stone and masonry, masonry blocks, or wood. It can form a backdrop for flower beds, a pool, or a rock garden.

STEPS are useful in retaining walls or where a walk goes down a slope. They can be made of many materials, but it may be best to follow the pattern you have set with your walk or wall. You can build beautiful steps from concrete, stone, brick, or wood.

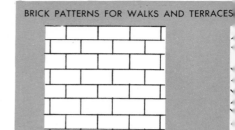

BRICK PATTERNS FOR WALKS AND TERRACES

RUNNING BOND

To lay brick paving, use brick or wood header. Fill joints between bricks with dry concrete mix and sprinkle with hose.

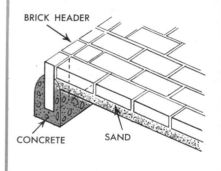

BRICK HEADER

CONCRETE   SAND

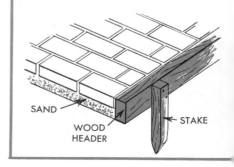

SAND

WOOD HEADER

STAKE

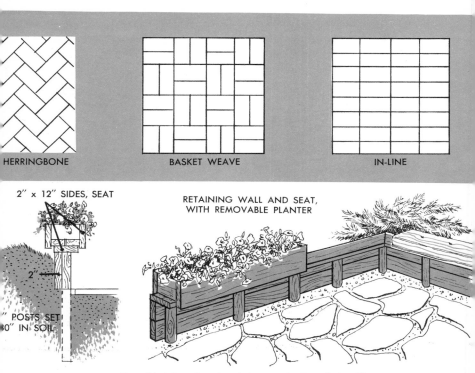

HERRINGBONE

BASKET WEAVE

IN-LINE

2″ x 12″ SIDES, SEAT

2″

POSTS SET
30″ IN SOIL

RETAINING WALL AND SEAT,
WITH REMOVABLE PLANTER

For added strength, set posts in concrete. Gravel at wall's
base provides better drainage. Planter can be removed
when flowers fade, replaced by another that has blooms.

vy and other ground covers
soften edges of steps.

Ground covers dress up
cinder-block retaining wall.

Comfort and Privacy. Trees, shrubbery, and fences can make your living area more private, cut off unpleasant views, and give you shade where you want it. In most yards, a *combination* of fences, trees, and shrubbery gives the best results. Here are some facts to help you decide where each will best fit into your plan.

TREES AND SHRUBS. Place trees where they will form a background and cut off unpleasant distant views. Use shrubs where you need a lower screen to cut off nearby areas.

Trees and shrubs, used as a screen, have a big advantage over fences. Their foliage and flowers can give you a beautiful and changing color scheme all through the season.

FENCES. Though you may prefer the natural look of trees and shrubs, don't sell fencing short. It has many advantages over a growing screen:

1. A fence takes up only about 6 inches of width, while shrubs should have at least 3 feet.

2. Shrub roots often rob adjacent flower beds of moisture and food.

3. A fence can be put up in a few days; it takes years to grow a screen with shrubbery. Consider using a fence while shrubbery is growing to full size.

4. Fences can give an interesting effect during the season when most plants have no leaves or flowers.

DECIDUOUS TREES PROVIDE COOL SHADE I

COMBINATION OF FENCE AND

NEIGHBOR · PROPERTY LINE

Evergreens, flowers, and ground cover make an attractive boundary planting.

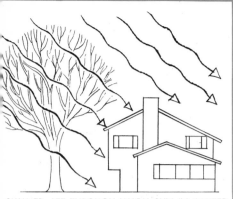

SUMMER, LET THROUGH WARM SUN IN WINTER

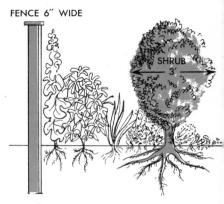

FENCE 6" WIDE

SHRUB 3'

SHRUBS TAKE MORE SPACE THAN FENCES, ROB PLANTS OF MOISTURE AND FOOD

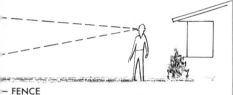

— FENCE
SHRUBS OR TREES INCREASES PRIVACY

BAMBOO FENCE MAKES A GOOD SCREEN

Fence plus plants along property line provide beauty as well as privacy.

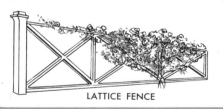

LATTICE FENCE

BASKET WEAVE FENCE

Planning Your Grounds • 15

Planning and Building a Lily Pool. A water garden adds refreshing variety to a yard. The pool doesn't have to be large—small and medium lilies will do well even in tubs. But there are many water plants you can try, so be generous with the space you allow. Ideal depth of a pool is 16 to 24 inches.

Locate the pool where it will get full sun. Lilies will not bloom unless the sun shines into the heart of them at least part of the day. The corner of the yard or end of the flower border are two favorite locations. A fence or stone wall makes a nice backdrop. Shrubs in back of the pool may grow too large and shade the lilies, besides filling the pool with leaves.

BUILDING A SIMPLE POOL   After deciding shape and size, dig out soil to a depth of 2 feet. Shave sides to as near perpendicular as possible. Walls that slope waste space, and algae forms on them.

Tamp the walls and floor. Reinforce them with heavy stucco wire. Cover the wire with 1 to 1½ inches of cement. Then pull the wire through to the surface of the cement, leaving the cement very rough.

Apply a second coat of cement. The wire now lies between the two coats. Smooth the second coat with a trowel and an old paint brush. In cold regions, the cement should be 6 inches thick; in warm regions, 3 inches.

Next seal with pure plastic cement and water. This mixture should be the consistency of thin paint. It is made with one shovel of cement to five of sand.

Fill the pool with water and let it stand for three days. Add a quart of vinegar to each 100 gallons of water to neutralize the alkalinity of the concrete so the pool will be safe for fish. Drain and refill with plain water. Now the pool is ready to plant.

Keep a half dozen fish in the pool for each 6 square feet of area. They will eat all mosquito larvae. Goldfish are fine.

PLANTING LILIES   Use a bushel or so of soil at the bottom of the pool or in a box for each lily. A good mixture is ¼ well-rotted dairy fertilizer and ¾ good loam. Hardy lilies can be set out from February through October in frost-free areas; from April 1 to August 1 in frost areas. Tropical lilies should be set out only after nights remain warm.

Hardy lilies may be wintered in the pool if the roots do not freeze. In cold areas, cover pool with boards and put straw over them. If you think there is still danger of freezing, store the lilies in a cool cellar before cold weather arrives. Be careful that they don't dry out.

Backdrop of evergreens *sets off this concrete pool. Sky-blue concrete enamel adds life and beauty. Planting includes: day- and night-blooming water lilies, water hyacinths, and water poppies for color; various shallow-water and bog plants for contrast. Note that some of water is left unplanted for reflection. Below: Three varieties of water lilies, which come in many colors and sizes.*

Lavish use of azaleas and other evergreens in this Alabama yard (above) *provides flowers in season and handsome foliage the rest of the year.* Below: *Inviting terrace greets callers to this Florida home. Long-blooming evergreen allamanda, a yellow-flowered vine, clambers on wooden rail fence.*

Azaleas, rhododendrons, and other evergreens (above) *make an effective foundation planting around Long Island home.* Right and below: *Muted tones of slate walks are intensified by colors of nearby plantings.*

Picture-book setting (left) *is provided by well-planned landscaping around this country home. Rock retaining wall and oak tree in foreground frame an uncluttered, spacious expanse of lawn. Flower border is located so that it can be seen from windows and enclosed terrace. Lilies, phlox, Shasta daisies, day lilies, and other perennials provide summer-long bloom for outdoor decoration and cuttings for indoor arrangements.*

Trees frame this California house (above). *Everblooming roses give cheerful welcome at gate. White irises march down path leading to front door.* Below: *Fall garden of New York country home features chrysanthemums behind permanent edging of evergreen boxwood. In summer, the same beds display flowering annuals and perennials. Stone wall and steps add interest to garden.*

Flowering trees and shrubs *proclaim spring's arrival.* Above: *Flowering dogwood towers over harmonizing border of azaleas and other flowering shrubs.* Below, left to right: *Three favorites—Japanese tree peony, lilac, and azalea.*

Handsome rhododendron *beside path to front door (left) is an evergreen that can be depended upon for year-round attractiveness. It grows well in shaded areas and does best in acid soil.*

Foundation planting *of flowering shrubs and evergreens (right) adds to beauty of home. Below: Generous use of white-flowered azaleas provides contrast with pink and rose of other azaleas, rhododendrons.*

Blue of water (above) *provides heavenly background for azaleas. Rock path leads garden visitor to close-up view. Low rock-garden plants provide interest along way. Right: Front walk is embellished by hyacinths and daffodils in early spring, followed by summer-blooming annuals, then dwarf asters and mums in fall.*

Garden walls and fences *are enhanced by flowering plants. Rock wall below is outstanding example, with its Basket of Gold alyssum, candytuft, pansies, forget-me-nots, and woods phlox.*

Landscaping can do much *to dress up a driveway. Above: Planting at entrance of California driveway makes intelligent use of always-in-bloom geraniums. Below: A more austere setting in Massachusetts has neatly trimmed lawn accented by evergreens, flowers, and lawn furniture.*

Perennial border along driveway (right) *utilizes plants that are attractive from spring through fall. In late May, as shown, delphiniums, foxglove, columbine, irises fill in the bed behind pansies, pinks, and other edging plants, which spill over the driveway for a softening effect.* Below: *Bright-foliaged caladiums create a welcome at this driveway entrance, which is shaded from hot noonday sun.*

Swimming pools *can be a delight to the eye as well as the body.* Above: *Stepping stones on sand are functional, attractive. At left is outdoor dressing room.* Below: *Annual flowers complete this cheerful setting for outdoor living.*

Garden and house *seem planned to compliment this smartly shaped pool. A few choice plants comprise the border planting, require minimum care.*

Outdoor terrace (right) *is enriched by surroundings that are restful to the eye, yet of enough diverse interest to stimulate conversation. Shrub trimmed to the shape of a rooster seldom fails to stir comments from visitors. Note the use of potted plants in bloom to add touches of color to terrace.*

Who wouldn't like to laze *in the warm spring sun on this dazzling white terrace? Whitewashed wall shows off brickwork design and provides photogenic backdrop for colorful tulips.*

Formal rows of tulips, dwarf box (left) *are colorful border for path.* Below: *Oriental poppies light up a border of June-flowering perennials.* Right: *Bed of chrysanthemums against decorative redwood fence.*

Flower colors may be contrasting, harmonizing, or blending, as long as the overall effect is pleasing to the eye. Use spots of brilliance or groups of tall plants to relieve monotony of a bed or border, as shown on these pages.

Masses of phlox edged with large-leaf caladiums (left) *bring August color to walled Northeast garden.* Right: *Two approaches to color are shown in these photographs—tapestry of chrysanthemums in unrelated but harmonious shades; scarlet salvia and dwarf dahlias blend lavender petunias and golden marigolds along white picket fence.*

Your Lawn

There's nothing like a rich green lawn to set off the beauty of a flower garden or to make a house more inviting and attractive. And there's nothing like a thick healthy lawn to add comfort to outdoor living and to provide a carpet for games and other recreation.

These are fairly obvious facts, and it's not surprising that we Americans spend millions of dollars each year on lawn care. Yet, a good lawn is a rarity. Too many lawns are ragged, thin, and marred by bare spots.

A lawn may seem a rather temporary part of your landscape, as compared to trees and shrubs. But if a lawn is started right and given the proper care, it can be even more permanent than your trees.

Creating and keeping a good lawn is not an especially difficult task, though it does require more than an occasional scattering of grass seed and regular mowing. It takes some time, effort, and, most important, know-how. If you apply these, your lawn problem can be licked, whether you're starting with a stretch of bare earth surrounding a new house or with an old lawn that badly needs sprucing up.

How to Start a New Lawn. The best time to start a new lawn is in fall or spring, when the weather is cool and damp. Grass is hard to start when the weather is hot and dry, and when there is competition from weeds.

To start a healthy lawn you need a 4-inch layer of loam or sandy loam topsoil fairly rich in organic matter. Loam is an easily crumbled mixture of sand, clay, and organic matter.

On a new site where all topsoil has been scraped away, you may need to bring in new soil. But whenever possible, it is better to improve the soil you have rather than to buy new soil.

Not only is new soil fairly expensive, but good soil is hard to tell from poor when you're buying it. Even the best may contain weed seeds. Dark color alone does not mean soil is fertile or that it contains organic matter. Some black-dirt dealers use soot or other black material to darken soil. Muck soils are black, but not good for lawns unless mixed with other soils.

PREPARING THE SOIL To improve the topsoil you have, add organic matter. Use 500 to 1,000 pounds of well-rotted barnyard manure per 1,000 square feet of ground. Or spread a 2-inch layer of sewage sludge, peat moss, or compost over the ground. Mix this organic matter into the top 4 inches of soil.

Since grass does not grow well in water-logged soil, you must consider drainage. Unless your soil is a sandy loam, it should slope ½ inch per foot to allow water to drain away. Low areas in which there is heavy soil may have to be drained by tile pipes installed under the ground.

Before seeding, fertilize the soil. Use 10 to 15 pounds of a turfgrass fertilizer per 1,000 square feet. Mix it thoroughly with the top 2 to 3 inches of soil. Any high-nitrogen grade of fertilizer, such as 12-6-6 or 10-6-4, will do a good job.

WHEN AND HOW TO SEED Roll and rake the soil's surface until you have a firm seedbed. On the last raking, the rake's teeth should not penetrate the soil to a depth of more than ¼ inch.

Seed can be spread by hand or with a seeder. Use 2 to 4 pounds of seed for each 1,000 square feet. Mix it with a small amount of screened sand for evener distribution. Rake lightly to cover the seed with ¼ to ⅛ inch of soil, and firm the seedbed by rolling.

Mulching the soil with a *light* covering of straw will help hold moisture and prevent washing. Since seedlings will die if they dry out, keep them moist by watering, whenever necessary, until they are well established. But avoid saturating the soil, for this favors fungus diseases.

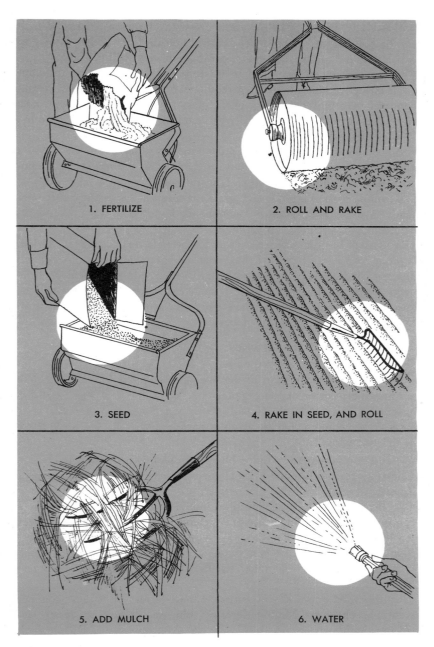

1. FERTILIZE

2. ROLL AND RAKE

3. SEED

4. RAKE IN SEED, AND ROLL

5. ADD MULCH

6. WATER

Which Grass to Plant. There are many kinds of grasses. Which are the best for your lawn depends largely on the part of the country in which you live and on the amount of sun your lawn will get.

Grass seed is generally sold in mixtures containing several different kinds of seeds to fit various lawn requirements. Be sure the mixture you buy contains a high percentage of the grasses recommended for your area and need. Avoid mixtures with large amounts of rye grass and timothy. Read the label carefully.

A good lawn in the North has predominantly bluegrass in the sun and a fescue in the shade. Best fescues for shady areas are red fescue, Pennlawn fescue, and Chewings fescue, in that order.

Bermuda grass is a good basic grass for sunny areas in the South. For shady areas, Manila grass is recommended in the mid-South and St. Augustine grass in the deep South.

A strain of Kentucky bluegrass that has become very popular is Merion. It produces a dark green turf that resists crabgrass, leaf spot disease, and drought conditions. It also grows better in the shade than common Kentucky bluegrass. Though Merion is more expensive than common bluegrass and is harder to grow, since it requires a more fertile soil, it is an excellent choice if given the proper care.

Climate Guide for Grasses.

To find out what grasses to use for your lawn, check the map to determine the number of the region in which you live. Grasses suitable for each numbered region are given in the following list.

1 and 5: common and Merion bluegrass, colonial bent grass, red fescue, Chewings fescue. Limited areas of these regions: Bermuda grass, Meyer Zoysia.

2: Bermuda grass, Zoysia grasses. Limited areas of region: Carpet grass, centipede grass, St. Augustine grass, common Kentucky bluegrass, Merion Kentucky bluegrass.

3: Nonirrigated areas: blue grama grass, buffalo grass, crested wheat grass. Irrigated areas: common Kentucky bluegrass, Merion Kentucky bluegrass.

4: Bermuda grass, Zoysia grasses. Limited areas of region: common Kentucky bluegrass, Merion Kentucky bluegrass, Chewings fescue, red fescue, Pennlawn fescue.

Care and Grooming of Your Lawn. Of the many things that contribute to the health of a lawn, fertilizer and water are of key importance. A lawn that's well fed will resist disease, compete successfully with weeds, and get thicker every year.

WHEN AND HOW TO FERTILIZE Nitrogen is usually the most needed nutrient for old lawns. However, unless you've had the soil tested, and the test shows a need for a nitrogen fertilizer, it's better to use a complete fertilizer with a high nitrogen content, such as a 12-6-6 (12 per cent nitrogen, 6 per cent phosphorus, 6 per cent potash).

In the North, apply the fertilizer 3 times—March 1, June 1, and September 1 to 15. For each 1,000 square feet, use 5 pounds of fertilizer for fescues, 10 pounds for Kentucky bluegrass, and 20 pounds for Merion. Or try the new mixed ureaforms. Though more expensive, they need be applied only once a year, in spring, yet feed the grass all season long. Use 20 pounds of a 20-5-5 ureaform per 1,000 square feet for any grass.

In the South, apply a complete fertilizer twice: in spring, when grass begins to grow; and in fall, 30 days before the first average frost date. Use 15 to 20 pounds of a complete fertilizer per 1,000 square feet. In addition, Bermuda, St. Augustine, and Zoysia lawns need 1 pound of nitrogen fertilizer per 1,000 square feet every 20 to 30 days during the growing season.

Do not fertilize when the grass is wet. Otherwise the fertilizer may stick to the grass and burn it. Water the lawn immediately afterwards to wash the fertilizer off the leaves.

WHEN AND HOW TO WATER Wait until the grass is almost suffering from lack of water, then soak the soil to a depth of 6 inches or more. To soak 6 inches you'll need to apply ⅜ inch of water on sand, ¾ inch on loam, and 1¼ inches on heavy clay.

If there's no rain, sand will need this soaking every 4 to 5 days, loam every 7 to 10 days, and clay every 12 to 18 days.

Here's how to tell how much water your sprinkler is delivering. Put a can near the sprinkler, another near the edge of the area being covered, and a third between these two. Run the sprinkler an hour, measure the depth of water in the cans, and average it out. Deep soaking helps develop a strong, deep root system. Light sprinkling encourages shallow roots and stimulates weeds.

REMOVING RUBBISH If leaves, branches, or grass pile up on your lawn, they can smother the grass. Remove all such rubbish in the fall. In early spring, use the mower with a catcher to remove dead grass.

THICKENING A LAWN You can add new seed to a thin lawn without digging up the grass you have. Best time is early fall or early spring.

Rake the lawn vigorously with a steel garden rake to remove dead grass and scar the soil's surface. Spread seed, using about ¼ of the amount necessary for a new seeding. Sprinkle with water to settle the soil around the seed.

TO ROLL OR NOT TO ROLL The sight of a homeowner breaking his back pushing a 500-pound roller is as familiar in spring as the first robin. Unfortunately, he is making more trouble for himself than he is preventing.

Next to crabgrass the worst enemy of lawns is compaction. The roller packs soil, drives out air, and makes it hard for roots to grow. The only time a roller is needed on an established lawn is in early spring to press down *lightly* small clumps of grass that have risen above the ground level.

To correct compaction problems see if a local landscape gardener will rent you a lawn aerator. This device tears out bits of sod or cuts through tight sod, loosening the soil so the roots of grass can get air.

MOWING GUIDE

Mow grass often, leaving the clippings on the lawn. If grass grows tall, cutting is a shock that weakens it. Also, clippings must then be removed to prevent smothering the grass. Best height to mow varies with the variety of grass you have:

Variety	*Height*
Common Kentucky bluegrass	1½ in.
Merion bluegrass	1 in.
Fescues	1¼ in.
Bent grasses	¾ in.
New Bermuda grasses	¾ in.
Zoysias	1 in.
St. Augustine grass	1 in.

CONTROLLING LAWN ENEMIES Fertilizing and mowing will usually keep weeds under control. If not, there are many new chemicals that kill weeds without harming grass. Use them according to the manufacturer's directions. Controlling other enemies may require different means.

DANDELION

BROADLEAF WEEDS such as dandelion, plantain, and buckhorn can be controlled with 2,4-D. Early spring and early fall are the best seasons to use it.

Sodium salt or amine forms of 2,4-D are safest for home use. Ester forms are more efficient if used carefully. Sprays are more effective and less expensive than dusts.

CRABGRASS is tough to kill. Best method is to apply calcium arsenate in winter or early spring. This prevents crabgrass seeds from germinating. The treatment is of no value if applied after apple blossom buds show color. One application of calcium arsenate will kill sprouting crabgrass seed throughout the season. In dry form the chemical may be mixed with a fertilizer and applied with a spreader.

During the growing season try Sodar (DSMA). Apply it in spring when seedlings are making their first appearance or in fall when plants are forming seed heads. Give 3 to 5 treatments at 10-day intervals.

CRABGRASS

CHICKWEED cannot always be completely controlled with chemicals. A combination of 2,4-D and Sodar will kill it at temperatures above 70°. Apply on a warm day in late fall when grasses are dormant and chickweed is growing.

CHICKWEED

ANTS AND WHITE GRUBS can be fought with chlordane, dieldren, heptachlor, or aldrin. Water or cultivate the chemical into the soil after applying it.

MOLES AND POCKET GOPHERS can be discouraged by destroying ants and white grubs, which they eat. Traps placed in mole tunnels are effective. Poison baits work well against pocket gophers but not so well against moles.

Ground Covers for Trouble Spots. On steep, hard-to-mow slopes or in deep shade where grass is hard to grow, try a ground cover other than grass. Many ground covers are easier to grow and care for than grass. When planting them, prepare the soil as you would for any flower border and add fertilizer and humus. Here's the U.S. Department of Agriculture list of ground covers, including their popular and scientific names:

Plants for Shade Only
Japanese Spurge (Pachysandra terminalis)
English Ivy (Hedera helix)
Stonecrop (Sedum ternatum)
Wild Ginger (Asarum canadense)

WILD GINGER

For Sun or Shade
Bugle (Ajuga reptans)
Forget-me-not (Myosotis semperflorens)
Germander (Teucrium chamaedrys)
Lily of the Valley (Convallaria majalis)
Periwinkle (Vinca minor)
Rock Speedwell (Veronica Teucrium or
 V. rupestris)
Sweet Woodruff (Asperula odorata)
Wintercreeper (Euonymus fortunei)

LILY OF THE VALLEY

For Sun Only
Buttercup (Ranunculus acris)
Maiden Pink (Dianthus deltoides)
Moss Pink (Phlox subulata)
Snow-in-summer (Cerastium tomentosum)
Stonecrop (Sedum acre, S. album, or
 S. spurium)
Thyme (Thymus serpyllum)

STONECROP

Your Trees and Shrubs

Trees and shrubs not only add beauty to a landscape and provide welcome shade, but they can also serve as a windbreak and a screen for privacy. You'll want to keep these points in mind when you choose trees and shrubs for your yard. You'll also want to stay within the limits of what grows well in your climate and to know any drawbacks that particular trees or shrubs may have from your point of view.

Some trees and shrubs spread too fast, forming dense growth at the expense of other plants. Others, like the sycamore, shed their leaves very early in the fall, creating a raking job.

Before you buy, consider whether the tree or shrub will grow too large for its location, whether it will thrive in the soil in which it will be planted, and whether it will do best in sun or shade. If you want fast growth, you may have to sacrifice other things. Chinese elm, for example, will give you shade in a few years, but its branches break easily.

The shape of each tree and shrub (see next page) should contribute to your landscape picture. Your local nurseryman or a nearby agricultural college can suggest suitable plants for your various needs.

Basic Shapes of Trees and Shrubs

DECIDUOUS SHRUBS

SPREADING

ROUND

UPRIGHT

DECIDUOUS TREES

ROUND

WEEPING

OVAL

VASE

ERECT

PYRAMIDAL

EVERGREENS

CREEPING

SPREADING

ROUND

COLUMNAR

NARROW PYRAMIDAL

BROAD PYRAMIDAL

Planting and Transplanting Trees and Shrubs. Trees and shrubs should be planted or transplanted in the spring or fall when they are inactive.

PLANTING   Dig a hole with straight sides, making it large enough so roots can fan out to a natural position. Plant evergreens the same depth as they were in the nursery. Plant deciduous trees and shrubs 1 to 2 inches deeper. For balled and burlaped plants, make the hole 12 inches wider and 3 inches deeper than needed for the ball. Fill in the 3 inches with moist topsoil.

Cover the roots of unballed plants with moist topsoil, packing it in and around the roots with your hands. Be sure there are no air pockets left around the roots.

Burlap can be left on balled plants, but loosen it at the top. Remove plants from containers, but keep the soil around the roots intact.

As you fill the hole, pack down the soil with your foot after every few shovelfuls. Leave a basin around the trunk for water the first season. Fill it with soil for the first winter.

TRANSPLANTING   When moving trees and shrubs, it is wise to ball and burlap their roots, especially if the plants are very large. The ball should be 1 foot wide for every inch the trunk is in diameter, as measured 1 foot above the ground. Dig a trench around the tree and bind the roots, as shown in the drawings. If the roots are exposed to air, the plant may dry out and die. Plant as described above. If you are not planting the tree or shrub right away, keep its roots damp.

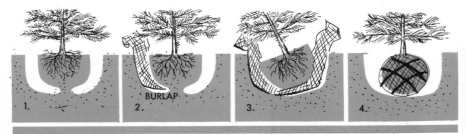

Fertilizer Guide for Trees and Shrubs. Make the first application of fertilizer in early spring when leaves are coming out. Fertilize again in mid-August. This is the most important feeding of the year, for woody plants are beginning to store food for the next year's growth. Use the same amount of fertilizer for each feeding. A complete fertilizer with a high nitrogen content, such as one with a formula of 10-6-4 or 10-5-5, is recommended for feeding deciduous trees and shrubs.

TREES   A general rule is to use 1 to 3 pounds of fertilizer for each inch of tree diameter. Measure the diameter 2 or 3 feet from the ground. Use the smaller amount for young trees and the larger amount for older trees.

To apply fertilizer, use an iron bar or sharp stake that is 1 to 1½ inches in diameter to make holes 12 to 18 inches deep around the tree. Start 3 feet from the trunk. Make holes 2 feet apart until they extend beyond the spread of the branches.

Place 2 heaping tablespoons of fertilizer in each hole. Add water to dissolve the fertilizer. Spread the remaining fertilizer on the surface.

FLOWERING SHRUBS   Use ¼ to ½ cup of fertilizer for each square yard of ground under the shrubs. The smaller amount is satisfactory for healthy shrubs. Be careful not to get any fertilizer on the stems. Work it lightly into the soil with a rake.

EVERGREENS   These can be harmed by too much fertilizer, so be careful. Organic fertilizer or well-rotted manure may be best. Use 2 pounds of either of these for each inch of trunk diameter.

A low-analysis mineral fertilizer, such as 3-2-1 or 4-6-4, can be used in the amount of ¼ cup per square yard under the tree. Or cottonseed meal can be applied, using ½ cup per square yard.

Pruning Guide for Trees and Shrubs. Trees and shrubs are pruned to control their shape; to remove dead, injured, or diseased branches; to limit their size; and to improve their vigor and appearance. The need for pruning depends on the type of plant.

PINES, SPRUCES, AND FIRS These seldom need pruning, though sometimes their appearance can be improved by it. To reduce open space at the top of the tree, cut off half of the leader in spring when it is half developed. Do not cut before the new growth starts or after it is nearly mature. This would stop the leader from growing. If the tree develops more than one leader, cut off all but the best.

To replace a lost leader, attach one of the branches at the side of the leader to a vertical brace. Tie with strips of cloth wound around the branch and brace in a figure 8. Put the brace on the tree in spring when branches are flexible. Remove it after one growing season.

To make the tree more bushy and keep side branches from growing out of bounds, pinch off the terminal buds. If the tree is already too wide, cut branches back to the inner buds.

JUNIPERS, YEWS, ARBORVITAES, HEMLOCKS, CEDARS Practically all of these plants need pruning. Clip them early in the spring or fall, beginning a year after they were bought from the nursery. If they need little pruning, wait until late in either season.

To shape, start pruning when the shrub is young. By pruning every year you'll need to remove only the ends of the branches.

On plants that are already too big, cut long branches back to an inner side branch carrying generous foliage. Branches will spread and fill in any open areas.

HEDGES   Cut a hedge down to 6 inches right after planting. Allow it to grow the first season with no summer pruning.

At the end of the first growing season, cut the hedge back to 12 inches. During the next summer cut it back to 18 inches.

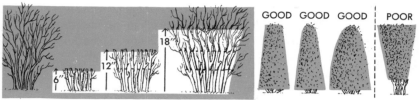

GOOD   GOOD   GOOD | POOR

Shape the hedge so that it is wide at the bottom, as in the first three drawings above, right. A wide base allows the sun to reach the leaves at the foot of the hedge. The shape of the hedge in the last drawing is poor because the wide top shades the base, resulting in bare stems.

LARGE SHADE TREES   It's best to prune shade trees in late spring or early summer. Cut small branches (under 1 inch in diameter) flush to the main branch or trunk with a saw or pruning shears. To prevent tearing of the bark, remove larger branches in three separate cuts:

WRONG WAY   RIGHT WAY

1. Make a cut on the underside about 1 foot out from where the branch joins the trunk. Cut at least ¼ through the branch.

2. Cut off the branch from the top 1 or 2 inches out from the first cut.

3. Cut off the remaining stub flush with tree trunk.

PROTECTING WOUNDED TREES   Trim out bark above and below large cuts and wounds caused by pruning or natural events. Then cover the surface with a substance to protect it against insects and disease until the bark grows over.

Orange shellac makes a quick, tight seal. Pine tar is excellent, as

is a good tree asphalt paint. Repaint open wounds each year until they are healed.

Protect Evergreens for Winter. A severe northern winter takes its toll on evergreens in two ways: winter burn and breakage from ice and snow. Winter burn is a drying injury caused by needles losing moisture faster than roots can replace it. Entire limbs may die.

An August feeding with fertilizer increases the winter hardiness of evergreens. In August, evergreens stop growing at the tips of their branches, and twigs begin to increase in diameter, storing food for the winter. This stored food apparently bolsters an evergreen's resistance to winter harm.

In addition to building up the health of the plants, you can take the following steps:

1. Water evergreens deeply before the soil freezes, and mulch them to slow down water loss. Extra water reduces chances of winter burn. Where the soil is dry, it may be necessary to water the plants during winter thaws.

2. Use a temporary screen to protect fall-planted evergreens from winter winds.

3. Drive a stake next to tall shrubs and tie them up. This can save them from being bent or broken by ice or snow.

4. In winter, brush off snow right after it falls, when it is still powdery. The ice that forms from the thawing and freezing of this snow causes the damage. Once formed, ice is hard to remove.

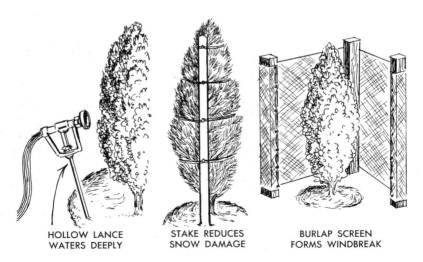

HOLLOW LANCE
WATERS DEEPLY

STAKE REDUCES
SNOW DAMAGE

BURLAP SCREEN
FORMS WINDBREAK

Your Flower Garden

The goal of most spare-time gardeners is to have flowers blooming throughout the growing season. This is more difficult in
smaller gardens, but it is possible to select and plant flowers so
that there will be a number of displays of blooms at times when
the family will most enjoy them.

If you are a beginning gardener, don't get overambitious the
first year. Select easy-to-grow annuals that are not too finicky
about amount of moisture, temperature, or kind of soil. Begin by
planting these, along with a few perennials and bulbs.

Starting a garden need not be hard on the budget if you con-
centrate on annuals. Perennials and bulbs can be added gradually from season to season. Friends will often offer you some
of their extras. Your own bulbs and perennials will multiply, so
mark the spots where they are planted and fill in the gaps with
annuals while your permanent flowers are spreading.

Naturally, flower beds should be located where there is plenty
of sun. A good loamy soil is important, but remember that poor
soil can be improved with humus or peat. Avoid places where
there is poor drainage. A background in the form of a fence,
shrubs, or wall will shelter the flowers from wind and help prevent breakage. By all means plant flowers where you can see and
enjoy them from the living room, dining area, or terrace.

Annuals—for Inexpensive Blooms. Whether you have a large estate or only a window box, you can have a profusion of blossoms for very little cost by planting annuals—the plants that grow from seed, bloom, produce seed, and die, all in one growing season. We estimate that for a dollar investment you can have more than 10,000 blossoms of all colors, from early spring until late fall.

There are hundreds of varieties of annuals. Here is information on seventeen annuals that are especially worth growing.

CALENDULA

LARKSPUR

SWEET ALYSSUM

PLANT AS EARLY AS SOIL CAN BE WORKED

Sweet Pea: 4-8 ft. high . . . Keep soil shaded at roots . . . Good climber, vine will grow on string or wire . . . Very fragrant . . . New heat-resistant varieties available.

Calendula: 14-18 in. high . . . Excellent cut flower . . . Likes cool temperature . . . Yellow-orange . . . New hybrids resemble daisies.

Blazing Star: 2-3 ft. high . . . California wildflower new in home gardens . . . Blooms in Aug.-Sept. . . . 3-in. blossoms.

Sweet Alyssum: 4-18 in. high . . . Dwarf variety good for edging in lavender blue . . . All varieties fine for window boxes.

Larkspur: 3-5 ft. high . . . Flowers form on long spikes . . . Night temperatures should not exceed 55° during early growth.

Mignonette: 6 in. high . . . Small white, yellow, or red flowers . . . Delightfully fragrant.

Calliopsis: 1½-2½ ft. high . . . Excellent cut flower . . . Yellow and brownish-red . . . Dwarf varieties are only 9-15 in. high.

PLANT WHEN SOIL IS COOL,
BUT FROST UNLIKELY

Aster: 12-24 in. high . . . All colors except yellow and orange . . . Excellent cut flower.

ASTER

Cosmos: 3-4 ft. high . . . Six colors . . . Good background for border plantings . . . Continuous bloom in summer . . . Mandarin a new variety . . . Bright orange double blossoms.

Petunia: 8-24 in. high . . . Do not cover seed . . . Needs sunlight to germinate . . . Good for flower baskets . . . Will grow in poor soil.

PETUNIA

Cleome (Spiderflower): 30 in. high . . . Will grow in poor soil . . . Salmon pink color . . . Good background flower.

Bells of Ireland: 24-36 in. high . . . No actual blossom . . . When leaves are removed, bells are nice in flower arrangements.

MARIGOLD

PLANT IN WARM SOIL

Marigold: 6-36 in. high . . . African, French, or dwarf . . . Yellow and orange . . . Very easily grown . . . Tolerates heat.

Celosia: 12-24 in. high . . . Silky plumes in brilliant red, yellow, orange . . . Dries well for winter use.

Zinnia: 4-36 in. high . . . Usually drought resistant . . . All colors . . . Long-lasting cut flower.

Moss rose (Portulaca): 6-9 in. high . . . Five brilliant colors . . . Excellent for rock garden.

DWARF
ZINNIA

Annual dwarf dahlia: 12-24 in. high . . . Start seeds in house 6 weeks in advance, then transplant . . . Likes cool weather.

Planting Pointers for Annuals. In a few weeks tiny annual flower seeds expand their volumes thousands and thousands of times. This sensational growth requires a fertile soil, abundant moisture, and generally at least half of the day in full sunlight.

PREPARING THE SOIL Use a complete fertilizer, such as a 5-10-5 mixture, applying about 1½ pounds to 100 square feet. Work the fertilizer well into the soil before planting.

HOW DEEP TO PLANT A rule of thumb is: the smaller the seed, the shallower you plant it. Tiny petunia and snapdragon seeds are often sown on top of finely prepared soil, then covered with thin cheesecloth and kept damp until small seedlings are visible. Large seeds, such as nasturtium and sunflower, are planted ½ inch deep. For good results, try covering large seeds with about ¼ inch of sphagnum moss. It does not form a crust and holds moisture well.

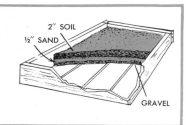

STARTING SEEDS INDOORS You can get a jump on the weather by starting seeds indoors in early spring. Use a box or pot that has adequate drainage. Or put a layer of gravel in the bottom, add ½ inch of sand, and fill with at least 2 inches of good soil. (You can buy sterile potting soil.)

Cover large seeds with ¼ inch of soil, vermiculite, or sphagnum moss. Put a cover on the box to hold moisture and hasten germination. Water soil whenever it shows signs of dryness. When plants come up, place them in sunlight. Transplant when second leaves form.

Some flowers, such as phlox, California poppies, larkspur, lupine, and sweet peas, do not respond well if moved after the seed germinates. Their seeds should be planted in peat fiber pots. The pots themselves can then be planted in the permanent location, which eliminates the risk of setting back the plants. Once in the soil, the pots gradually disintegrate.

MAKING A COLDFRAME   For an earlier and better garden in the north, build yourself a moderate-sized coldframe. With a few dollars' worth of boards and 2 x 4 stakes (even second-hand lumber will do) you can readily construct a frame 18 inches high at the back, 12 inches at the front, 4 to 6 feet wide, and 6 to 8 feet long. The frame is covered with glass sash.

Seeds can be planted in the coldframe several weeks before they can be planted outdoors. During the day the sash may be opened to prevent overheating; later it is closed to conserve heat during the night.

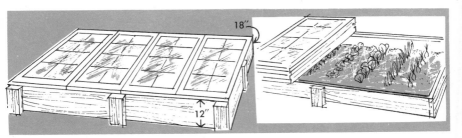

BUILDING A HOTBED   To get a really early start on your tender annuals (and vegetables, too), plant seeds in a hotbed after the first of the year. A hotbed is essentially a heated coldframe. The use of manure as a heat source has been largely supplanted by electric heating, which greatly improves growing conditions for seedlings. The drawings show two ways to heat a hotbed by electricity.

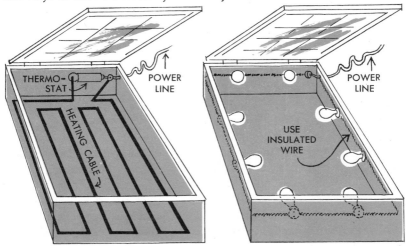

Perennials—for Early and Late Blossoms. Wherever there are cold winters, perennials can be relied upon to lengthen the flowering season. They bloom before the ground is warm enough and dry enough to plant annuals; and some perennial flowers last until the first hard freeze.

Most perennial flowers die to the ground in winter and come up again in spring. The plant lives during the cold weather through its roots and other underground parts.

Since perennials are an almost permanent part of the garden, they should be planted where soil will not need to be disturbed in the spring.

HOW TO PLANT A PEONY

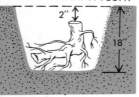

Work compost and fertilizer into bottom of hole. Set root as shown.

Add soil around root, then fill hole twice with water to settle soil.

Fill rest of hole with dry soil, mounding it slightly. Cover with mulch.

PLANTING   Perennials that bloom in the spring and summer are planted in the fall, while fall flowers are planted in the spring. To plant, work soil 18 inches deep and mix leaves, compost, or peat moss into it.

Fall planting and transplanting should be completed at least four weeks before the ground freezes to enable the plants to become firmly anchored. Iris and oriental poppies mature early and must be transplanted in late July. Peonies are transplanted about September 1. Delphiniums should never be transplanted in the fall.

FEEDING   Each spring add a top dressing of 2 pounds of a good mixed fertilizer per 10 square feet as a stimulant to healthy growth. Cultivate the soil only enough to keep down weeds. Mulch.

WATERING   If perennials are to make fast growth, they need a constant supply of moisture. Once a week, give them enough water to soak down 18 inches into the soil.

SPECIAL CARE   Do not permit flowers to go to seed unless seed is desired. This weakens the plant and stops the blooming period.

The tops of the plants should not be cut off in the fall, for this often exposes hollow stems and leads to the rotting of the roots.

Wait until the ground has frozen and field mice have built their winter homes before you add straw or leaves to protect perennials.

Four Popular Perennials

DAY LILY   In midsummer the perennial border generally has few blooms. Here, the fast-growing day lily (Hemerocallis) comes to the rescue with its summer flowers. It is now available not only in the familiar yellow and brownish-orange colors, but also in true pinks, near purples, reds, and various blends. A nice thing about this flower is that you can plant or transplant it when it's in full bloom.

IRIS   The large handsome flowers of the iris appear in late spring, giving the garden a welcome burst of color. After they have flowered and completed their early summer growth, they are ready to be divided, if overcrowded, and to be reset in July or August. In making divisions, discard the old rhizome (underground rootlike stem), replanting the new tip growths that have fresh root systems. To prevent early clumping, set new divisions in a triangular fashion with leaf fans pointing outward.

PEONY   A hardy, easy-to-grow perennial, the peony is a favorite among gardeners. Peonies can be grown in poor soil and in light shade, though they naturally thrive in full sun and in well-fertilized soil. Since the plants and their blooms are large, they look best in fairly spacious gardens. Late summer or early fall is the time to plant or transplant them. Divide old clumps into small pieces, each with three to five buds. Plant them 1 to 2 inches below soil level. If set too deep, they won't bloom.

PHLOX   In northern gardens from the East through the Midwest, phlox are a standby through much of the growing season. The various varieties may bloom from July into September. The plants thrive in full sun, but will do all right in light shade. Best time to plant or transplant them is in September. They can be propagated by dividing old clumps and by stem and root cuttings.

Flowering Bulbs—for Spring and Summer Blooms. Most flowering bulbs are perennials, in that they produce blooms year after year. But they are considered a special class, since they have a different method of storing energy during the winter. Flowering bulbs are a welcome addition to the garden not only because of their beauty, but also because they grow well under various conditions and require little care.

Among the flowering bulbs that bloom in spring are daffodils, tulips, hyacinths, bulb irises, crocuses, scillas, grape hyacinths, and snowdrops. Summer-flowering bulbs include begonias, dahlias, and gladioli.

PLANTING   Most spring-flowering bulbs are planted in the fall. Planting time of summer-flowering bulbs varies. Two popular summer-flowering bulbs, dahlias and glads, are planted from April to July, depending on the climate.

Bulbs prefer light, well-drained soil, usually a sunny location, and plenty of moisture. Soil should be worked to a depth of 12 inches, even though bulbs are set only 2 to 7 inches deep, depending on climate, soil, and size of bulb. Set bulbs firmly into the ground so there are no air pockets underneath. Water liberally.

FERTILIZING   Barnyard manures should not be used near bulbs because they cause bulbs to rot. Completely decomposed manure may be worked in at planting time or in the spring. A complete fertilizer, such as 5-10-5, may be applied in the proportion of 3 pounds per 100 square feet of ground.

CULTIVATING   Frequent shallow cultivation is necessary for weed control, and deep mulching is required for moisture retention.

CUTTING   Flowers last longer if cut with a sharp knife. When the plant's flowers fade, cut them off to prevent seed formation, which is a drain on the plant's energy. Bulbs develop best for next year's bloom if the leaves are not cut until three-fourths of them are dead.

DIGGING   Dig bulbs only when they become too crowded and produce small flowers. Dig spring-flowering bulbs in late summer and dry them slowly in an airy, shady location. Do not expose bulbs to sun. Divide the bulbs and replant them in the fall.

WINTERING   If winters are severe, protect spring-flowering bulbs with 2 to 4 inches of mulch after the ground is frozen to a depth of 1 to 2 inches. Some summer-flowering bulbs will not survive severe winters. The bulbs of dahlias and glads, for example, should be dug after the first frost and stored in dry sand or vermiculite in a cool, dry cellar. Dust these bulbs with 5 per cent DDT to prevent disease. Do not let them freeze.

How and Where to Plant Bulbs. This chart gives specific planting information for thirteen flowering bulbs that are among the most popular with gardeners.

Time of planting depends on the hardiness of the bulb. Bulbs hardy enough to withstand winter cold are planted in fall and bloom in spring. Less hardy bulbs are planted in spring and bloom in summer. Planting time may vary with climate and variety of plant.

Selection of the planting site will depend upon the variety of bulb. While most bulbous plants like a fairly sunny location, there are a few kinds that prefer light shade.

N. EP	SUN	SUN OR SEMI-SHADE	SEMI-SHADE	SPACING
			TUBEROUS BEGONIA (Spring Planting)	TUBEROUS BEGONIA 12"
1				
2		*ANEMONE (Fall Planting)	SNOWDROP (Fall Planting)	SNOWDROP 3" ANEMONE 4"-6"
3		BULB IRIS (Fall Planting)	CROCUS (Fall Planting)	BULB IRIS 6" CROCUS 3"
4		SCILLA (Fall Planting)		SCILLA 3"
5	GLADIOLUS (Spring Planting)			GLADIOLUS 6" HYACINTH 6"
6	DAHLIA (Spring Planting)	HYACINTH (Fall Planting)	NARCISSUS (Fall Planting)	DAHLIA 24"-36" NARCISSUS 6"
7			TULIP (Fall Planting)	TULIP 6"-8" DAFFODIL 6"-8"
8	DAFFODIL (Fall Planting)	LILY (Fall Planting)		LILY 12"

Soak in tap water for two or three hours before planting.

How to Plant and Care for Roses

PLANTING   Dig a hole at least 18 inches deep and 24 inches in diameter. Mix a quart of peat moss with the loosened soil at the bottom of the hole. Keep the plant's roots soaking in a bucket of water as you prepare the hole. Never leave roots exposed to sun and air. Prune off broken top growth and injured roots.

BUD UNION

SOIL LEVEL

Form a cone of soil in the hole to within 3 to 4 inches of ground level, so that the crown of the plant may rest on top of the cone without forcing the roots out of the position they naturally assume. Then work loose soil under and over the roots so there are no air pockets.

When the hole is three-fourths full, run water slowly into it until soil is settled. After water drains out, finish filling the hole.

In mild climates, plant so the bud union is at ground level after ground settles. (Ground will settle 1 to 2 inches.) If winters are severe, bud union should be 1 to 1½ inches below surface.

Protect canes temporarily from wind and from extremes of heat and cold by covering with wet burlap or by mounding loose damp soil or wet peat moss high around them. Keep the covering material moist by sprinkling. Remove it when new shoots appear on canes.

WATERING   Roses need lots of moisture. Water weekly when the ground is dry. Watering that wets the foliage should be done early in the day to allow the plant to dry by evening. Wet foliage encourages mildew. Best method is to let water flow slowly from a hose at the plant's base. Soak the soil to a depth of 18 inches.

FERTILIZING   Use about ½ cup of a complete fertilizer for one plant. Sprinkle it around the plant and scratch it into the soil, preferably just before a rain or a watering. Apply soon after the new spring growth is established and when all danger of freezing is past. If needed, a second application can be made later—but not later than August 15 in cold climates and September 15 in mild climates. Roses, which are not true woody plants, are an exception to the rule calling for a late feeding.

Roses prefer a slightly acid soil—about 6 to 6.6 pH. If a test shows that your soil has a higher pH than that, add a sprinkling of powdered sulfur; if lower, add lime.

PRUNING   Prune hybrid roses in late fall to a height of 15 to 24 inches. Use sharp pruning shears. In spring, when buds appear, prune canes back to ⅛ inch above bud or branch that is to be left. Try to save at least 10 inches of live wood. Usually prune to a bud facing outward. Cut off at ground level any dead canes not producing buds.

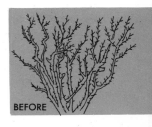

BEFORE

A cane generally produces good flowers for at least 4 or 5 years. When it ceases to do so, remove it entirely, allowing newer canes to take over.

Remove suckers below the bud union. Usually you can tell they're suckers because they have 7 leaflets to a leaf, while the plant itself has 5 leaflets.

AFTER

CONTROLLING PESTS   Roses are attacked by a wide variety of diseases and insects. To be safe, dust or spray your roses regularly with any good commercial rose dust that fights both disease and insects. A fungicide-insecticide with Phaltan added is most effective. Dust every week and after every rain, starting when leaves appear in spring. Be sure to dust both upper and lower leaf surfaces. Do not treat during excessively high temperatures (above 90°), since plants may be damaged.

PROTECTING FROM COLD   After the ground is frozen an inch or two deep, mound soil around plants to a height of 6 inches and cover the bed with leaves or straw. Do not dig the soil from near the plants, since this might expose their roots.

Climbing roses may be protected by removing the canes from their supports, stretching them out on the ground, and covering them with leaves or straw.

Tree roses may be tipped over into prepared trenches by loosening the roots from the soil on the opposite side. Or the trees may be taken up completely, placed in trenches, and covered.

Plant a Mobile Garden. There are many spots in the outdoor living area where plants in pots or other containers are more suitable than plants rooted in the ground. For portable containers allow you to have plants in flower, *all* the time, *exactly* where you want them. As the blooms fade, one set of plants may be replaced by pots containing plants in full flower.

Small flowering plants are not the only ones that can be planted in containers. Shrubs, roses, and small trees may be put in pots or tubs for outdoor use. In winter they can be taken inside to give a lift to the living room or can be stored in the basement.

Here are some tips on containers:

CLAY AND CERAMIC POTS are obvious possibilities. In addition to the usual clay pots, there are imported terra rossa pots with raised designs, and colorful glazed ceramic pots.

A SMALL WHEELBARROW filled with flowers can be a colorful addition to your lawn.

WOODEN BOXES made of redwood or cypress last well and make handsome containers for flowers. If the boxes contain potted plants set in beds of peat moss, the plants can be easily replaced when flowers fade.

STRAWBERRY CROCKS with plant "pockets" may be used to grow pansies or other small plants. Cacti and succulents are decorative when planted in the pockets.

TUBS made of half barrels or kegs are best for large shrubs, such as camellia and privet. Before use, they should be treated well with a wood preservative.

SUCCESS WITH CONTAINERS   The soil in a container should be loose enough to allow for drainage, humusy enough to retain some moisture. It should contain sufficient food to nourish plants according to individual plant need.

Pots should always drain well. Put a layer of broken pot pieces over the drain hole, then a layer of gravel or pebbles. Sphagnum moss will keep soil from washing down into the pebble layer.

All container plants need watering more often than plants grown in open ground. Water the plants at least every other day (except in rainy climates); in hot, dry weather, water every day or twice a day. Surest way of knowing pots are well watered is to place them in a bucket or tub of water until the pot ceases to send up bubbles. Doing this once a week, with a good dousing every other day, will usually be enough to keep plants in a healthy condition.

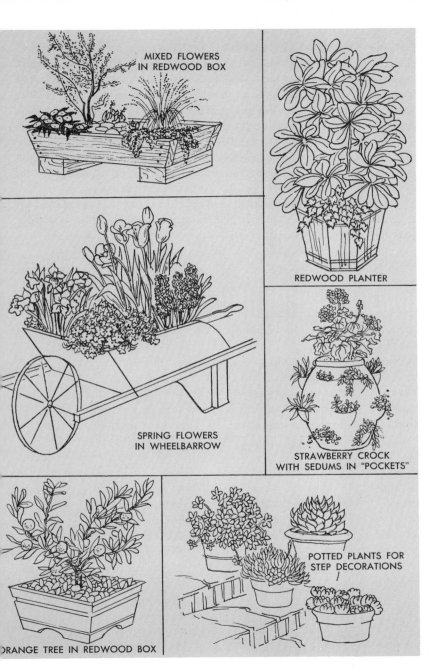

MIXED FLOWERS
IN REDWOOD BOX

REDWOOD PLANTER

SPRING FLOWERS
IN WHEELBARROW

STRAWBERRY CROCK
WITH SEDUMS IN "POCKETS"

POTTED PLANTS FOR
STEP DECORATIONS

ORANGE TREE IN REDWOOD BOX

Make Your Cut Flowers Last Longer. The problem of making cut flowers last longer has been tackled by Ruth Kistner, nationally known author, flower arranger, and lecturer. We present her own special formulas for doing this. They are taken from her excellent book, *Flower Arranging for the American Home* (Macrae Smith, Philadelphia), which she co-authored with Gladys Taber.

Mrs. Kistner advises: Gather flowers in the cool of evening or early morning. Keep them in a deep container filled with cool water, in a cool room free from drafts. When you are ready to arrange them, strip the stems of foliage for at least four inches from their base.

The following list gives special instructions for various flowers, including what to add to the water in which they are kept. Unless otherwise stated, qts., pts., etc., refer to water.

Achillia: 2 tbs. salt in 2 qts.

Aconitum (Monk's Hood): ½ cup vinegar in 2 qts.

Alyssum: 1 tbs. sugar in 2 qts.

Amaryllis: 2 tsp. kitchen ammonia in 1 qt.

Anemone: ½ cup vinegar in 2 cups.

Apple blossoms: Cut when in bud; crush stems; 2 tbs. ammonia in 2 qts.

Aquilegia (columbine): 5 drops oil of peppermint in 1 pt.

Asclepias (butterfly weed): 2 tsp. sugar in 1 qt. ice water.

Aster and all members of aster family: 2 tbs. sugar, 1 tbs. salt in 1 qt.

Baptisia: 5 drops hydrochloric acid in 1 qt.

Begonia: 2 tbs. salt in 2 qts.

Bird of paradise: ½ cup vinegar in 1 qt.

Bocconia (plume poppy): Burn ends of stems; ½ cup rock salt in 2 qts.

Camellia: Wrap in wet tissue over-night. These flowers never drink after being cut from plant.

Campanula (Canterbury bells): 2 tbs. washing soda in 2 qts.

Carnation: Cool water, up to flower heads. Don't submerge blooms.

Chrysanthemum: 10 drops oil of clover in 2 qts.

Clematis: 3 tbs. alcohol and a pinch of soda in 1 pt.

Coreopsis: 1 tbs. table salt in 1 qt.

Cosmos: 1 tsp. sugar in 1 pt.

Dahlia: Burn ends of stems; 5 tbs. alcohol in 2 qts. ice water.

Daisy (all types): 8 drops oil of peppermint in 1 qt.

Delphinium: 1 tbs. alcohol in 1 pt.

Dianthus: Same as for carnation.

Digitalis: 1 tbs. alcohol in 1 pt.

Evergreens (all types): 1 tbs. glycerine in 1 qt.

Fern: Submerge under water for 12 hrs. When ready to use, shake.

Forget-me-not: Plunge into hot, then cold water; 8 drops of alcohol in 1 pt.

Funkia and foliage (day lily): ½ cup vinegar in 2 cups cold water.

Gaillardia: 2 tbs. salt in 1 pt.

Gardenia: Do same as for camellia.

Gladiolus: 5 tbs. vinegar in 1 qt.

Grape hyacinth: plunge into hot, then cold water; 8 drops alcohol in 1 pt.

Gypsophila (babies'-breath): 1 tsp. alcohol in 1 pt.

Hollyhock: Burn ends of stems; 1 handful rock salt in 2 qts.

Hyacinth: Squeeze substance from end of stem as soon as bloom is picked. Plunge immediately into very cold water to which 5 drops oil of peppermint have been added.

Iris: 3 drops oil of peppermint in 1 qt.

Larkspur: 1 tbs. alcohol in 1 pt.

Liatris: Dip in 1 pt. water containing 3 tbs. lye.

Lilac: Never pull the green leaf off near flower head, as it conducts water to the bloom.

Lily (Easter, Regal, Hansoni, Grandiflorum, Henryi, and Calla): ½ cup vinegar in 2 qts.

Lily of the valley: ½ cup vinegar in 1 pt.

Marigold: 2 tbs. sugar, 1 tbs. salt in 1 qt.

Milkweed: Burn ends of stems; 1 handful rock salt in 2 qts.

Narcissus and family: Arrange in no more than 1 in. of water.

Peony: 3 tbs. sugar in 1 qt.

Petunia: 1 tsp. sugar in 1 pt.

Platycodon (balloon flower): ½ cup vinegar in 2 qts.

Poinsettia: Burn ends of stems; 1 handful rock salt in 2 qts.

Poppy: Same as for poinsettia.

Rose (all types): 2 tbs. powdered alum in 1 qt. If alum is not available, use 2 tbs. table salt in 1 qt.

Salvia: 1 tbs. alcohol in 1 pt.

Snapdragon: 2 tbs. salt in 2 qts.

Statice: 3 tbs. sugar in 1 qt.

Sweet Pea: Plunge into hot, then cold water; 8 drops of alcohol in 1 pt.

Tritoma: ½ cup vinegar in 1 qt.

Tulip: Roll in wet newspaper to keep stems straight. Place in cold water up to flower heads.

Violet: Bunch. Submerge for two hours after picking, then place in container filled with ice water.

Viola: Do same as for violet.

Water lily and lotus: 12 drops alcohol in 1 pt.

BOOKS ON
FLOWER ARRANGING

Flower Arrangement for Everyone, by Dorothy Biddle and Dorothea Blom (Barrows).

Creative Flower Arranging, by Margaret Carrick (Barrows).

Flower Arranging for the American Home, by Gladys Taber and Ruth Kistner (Macrae Smith).

A Treasury of Rose Arrangements and Recipes, by Julia Clements (Hearthside).

Indoor Gardening

Editor of the "Indoor Gardening" section is Elvin McDonald, who
has been active in gardening since his early boyhood on an Okla-
homa farm. A resident of Long Island, he is Eastern editor of
Flower & Garden Magazine. He handles all indoor gardening copy
for that publication and writes a monthly column called "In House
and Greenhouse."

Indoor gardening is not only an exciting, rewarding hobby, but
no house seems complete without healthy, growing plants. Mod-
ern homes, with central heating and large expanses of glass,
provide the basic ingredients for growing an endless array of
indoor plants. A window-sill garden can be as strangely enticing
as the bird-of-paradise plant or as friendly as red geraniums.

Things to Consider. In planning your indoor garden, consider these three basic growing conditions in your home: light, temperature, and humidity.

LIGHT   The amount of light your indoor area receives helps to determine what plants will thrive in it. And where you live affects how much light comes through your windows. For example, Denver, Colo., receives four more hours of sunlight a day during the winter than Cleveland, Ohio, or Bridgeport, Mich.

Local industry may make sunny days hazy. Reflective surfaces, such as a white house next door or a cement driveway, may direct more light through your windows. Trees and shrubs can make a south or west window suitable for shade-loving plants. Even clean windows make a difference.

For the light requirements of various plants, see the chart beginning on page 68.

TEMPERATURE   Most house plants thrive in a temperature range of 65 to 75 degrees. A few degrees above or below these figures shouldn't be harmful. If a plant requires cooler temperatures than you normally maintain in the home, keep it in a basement window, an unused guest room, or a sunporch.

HUMIDITY   An excessively dry atmosphere in the home is not only harmful to plants, but can damage your furniture and make your family uncomfortable. It's therefore wise to invest in an inexpensive humidity guide (sold in drugstores) to determine how much moisture is present. An average of 35 to 60 per cent is agreeable to most plants—and people, too.

You can increase the moisture in the air by having a humidifier attached to the furnace. Another way is to have a tinner construct galvanized trays 1 to 2 inches deep, or make your own from heavy aluminum sheets available at the hardware store. Paint the trays inside and out with waterproof paint. Place the trays wherever plants are to be grown, and fill them with vermiculite, pebbles, or peat moss. Keep this moist at all times. Group the plants in each tray, according to their height.

In extremely dry houses, an electric humidifier (the vaporizer used when children have a cold) is helpful when turned on for two or more hours daily. Use plain water in the humidifier.

A hand-operated plant fogger should be required equipment for all window gardeners. Keep the fogger full of water and spray the plants each day to keep them moist.

Gardening Under Lights. You don't need a sunny window to grow flowering plants indoors. Fluorescent lights can provide an inexpensive "sun" to grow flowers in a basement or dark corner.

The basic setup consists of a fluorescent unit of two to three 40-watt tubes in a 15-inch reflector. The unit is suspended 18 to 24 inches above a table on which plants are placed. Preferably the unit should be adjustable up and down.

The lights are turned on in the morning, off when you go to bed. They should burn 14 to 16 hours each day. An automatic timer (about $12) is handy for turning lights off and on, especially if you're away.

The list of plants that can be grown successfully under fluorescent lights is lengthy and exciting. A few of those most often grown are marked with double asterisks (**) in the table of outstanding indoor plants (pages 68-71).

THREE FLUORESCENT-LIGHT SETUPS: (1) SMALL DOUBLE-DECKER TABLE, (2) PLANTER-BOOKCASE, (3) LARGE TABLE FOR BASEMENT.

In Philadelphia, Pa., the Bruce Thompsons have made their basement into a breathtaking "greenhouse" by the use of fluorescent lights. The Thompsons grow hundreds of gloxinias and related plants on double-decker plant tables, each measuring 30 by 54 inches. Above each table top is suspended a fluorescent unit of three 40-watt tubes in a 15-inch reflector. From this basement have come many new hybrid plants worthy of distribution, including double-flowered gloxinias (see page 77).

When we began to decorate our new house, we found that one room, the den, had a drab personality. It faced north and always seemed dark. We solved the problem with a fluorescent-lighted bookcase.

It is 54 inches long and has two shelves for books and two fluorescent-lighted shelves, each with two 40-watt tubes, for plants. The insides of the two plant shelves are painted white for reflection. The rest of the bookcase is painted with a colored enamel to carry out the decorating scheme. The shelves are fitted with galvanized trays, 12 inches wide and 1 inch deep, to protect the wooden shelves from moisture. The trays are painted with white enamel. Colorful plastic pots complete the color scheme. Gloxinias, African violets, and begonias keep the shelves full of greenery and blossoms around the year.

What to do about Weak Winter Light. In January many house plants in the North begin producing long, weak shoots. The reason: they are stretching for light, which is at its weakest level in mid-winter.

If the plants are to remain healthy, the elements of growth—heat, light, water, and fertilizer—must be kept in balance. During winter months, when light is weak, cut down watering and feeding. Step them up again as the days lengthen. Do not move plants to a warmer, darker part of the room unless there is danger of freezing. Use artificial light if needed.

Plants Where Light is Poor.
Do you have a coffee table, mantle, or entranceway that needs living plant material to dress it up? Pass your hand across the table or surface. If your hand casts a faint shadow, there's probably enough light to grow the following: aluminum plant, artillery plant, ivy, peperomia, philodendron, pothos, rubber plant, dieffenbachia, nephthytis, Chinese evergreen, and possibly African violets.

If an entranceway is drafty, especially in the winter, cut some tough evergreen boughs to decorate it. Placed in water, they'll last almost indefinitely in the coolness and won't mind drafts from the opening door. Chunks of charcoal in the water will keep it fresh.

PHILODENDRON

DIEFFENBACHIA

OUTSTANDING INDOOR PLANTS

Plant	Amount of Light*	Best Temperature Range	When to Plant Seeds, Bulbs, Cuttings, etc.	Special Requirements	Bloom Time (If Any), Comments
Achimenes** (Nut-orchid)	Semi-sun	65-80°	Scaly tubercles, Feb.-April, 10-12 to 6" pot; keep warm.	Pinch off first growth to induce bushiness. Rest Nov.-Jan.	July-Oct.
Aechmea (Living vase plant)	Semi-shade	60-75°	Buy started plant.	Keep moist.	Handsome foliage; flowers in season.
African violet** (Saintpaulia)	Semi-sun	65-75°	Divisions and leaf cuttings may be started any time.	Constant humidity and bright light produce blooms.	Year-round.
Aluminum plant (Pilea cadierei)	Sunny or shady	60-75°	Cuttings any time.	Pinch to induce bushiness.	Attractive foliage.
Amaryllis**	Sunny	62-75°	Pot new bulbs Sept.-Dec.	Rest Sept.-Nov.	Dec.-March.
Ardisia crispa (Coral berry)	Shady	55-65°	Buy young plant.		Red berries; last two years.
Artillery plant (Pilea microphylla)	Semi-sun or shady	60-75°	Cuttings root easily any time.		Fern-like foliage.
Asparagus-fern (Asparagus plumosus or A. sprengeri)	Semi-sun	55-70°	Start any time by division.	Soak, allow to approach dryness, then soak again.	Foliage useful for flower arrangements.
Azalea**	Sunny	55-70°	Obtain started plants.	Coolness and high humidity. Place outdoors in summer.	Winter-spring, depending on variety.

OUTSTANDING INDOOR PLANTS

Plant	Amount of Light*	Best Temperature Range	When to Plant Seeds, Bulbs, Cuttings, etc.	Special Requirements	Bloom Time (If Any), Comments
Baby tears (Helxine soleiroli)	Semi-shade	60-75°	Press pieces of stem into fresh, moist soil any time.	Soak, allow to approach dryness, then soak again.	Ground cover for large pots or terrarium.
Begonia Christmas**	Semi-shade	55-70°	Cuttings in Nov.	Likes coolness and humidity.	Blooms for 90 days.
Fibrous-rooted and rhizomatous**	Sunny to shady	60-75°	Cuttings or seeds any time.	Moist, humusy soil.	Flowers at all times.
Rex**	Shady	65-75°	Divisions or leaf cuttings, March-Sept.	Warmth, high humidity.	Outstanding foliage.
Tuberous-rooted**	Shady	60-70°	Pot bulbs in Feb.; seeds in Jan.	Grow outdoors in shady, moist place. Rest tubers Nov.-Jan.	July-Oct.
Bird-of-paradise (Strelitzia reginae)	Semi-sun	60-75°	Divisions or suckers, Jan.-Aug.; use large pot or tub.	Keep dry, cool (55°), Nov.-Dec.	Spring-summer.
Bougainvillea	Sunny	60-75°	Cuttings any time; seeds sprout readily.	Prune to keep in bounds.	All year; blooms when young.
Caladium	Semi-sun	70-80°	Bulbs in spring or fall.	Humusy soil; lots of water. Rest 1-2 months each year.	Handsome foliage; 800 varieties.
Calceolaria** (Pocket-book plant)	Semi-sun	50-60°	Seeds in Aug. at 60°.	Coolness; spray weekly for aphids.	Winter, spring.

*Figure amount of light as follows: SUNNY—at least 5 hrs. daily in winter (south window); SEMI-SUN—2 hrs. daily in winter (east or west window); SEMI-SHADE—dappled sunlight or strong light (unshaded north window); SHADY—no sun, but light strong enough to cast shadow.
**Plant will thrive under fluorescent lights.

OUTSTANDING INDOOR PLANTS

Plant	Amount of Light*	Best Temperature Range	When to Plant Seeds, Bulbs, Cuttings, etc.	Special Requirements	Bloom Time (If Any), Comments
Calla lily	Sunny	60-70°	Bulbs, Aug.-Nov.	Humusy soil; lots of water.	Winter, spring
Camellia	Sun or semi-sun	45-55°	Buy plants from a specialist.	Keep evenly moist, high humidity. Soil pH 4 to 5.	Oct.-April, depending on variety.
Campanula isophylla (Star of Bethlehem)	Sunny (winter), semi-sun (summer)	55-70°	Cuttings in early spring.	Cut branches back after blooming.	Summer-fall.
Christmas cactus	Sunny (winter), semi-sun (summer)	60-75°	Cuttings any time.	Soil that drains perfectly.	Oct.-April.
Cissus** (many varieties)	Semi-sun or semi-shade	60-75°	Cuttings any time.	Reasonable amount of humidity.	Good foliage.
Crossandra**	Semi-sun	60-75°	Seeds any time.	Likes lots of humidity.	Spring-summer; orange flowers.
Episcia**	Semi-shade	65-80°	Cuttings, Jan.-Aug.	Likes warmth and humidity.	Foliage plants; bloom in summer.
Fuchsia**	Semi-sun	55-65°	Cuttings, early fall or spring.	Must be cool; needs humidity.	Flowers spring and summer.
Gardenia	Sunny	65-75°	Cuttings can be rooted in water, Jan.-Sept.	Needs high humidity; well-drained, moist soil. Summer indoors.	Oct.-June.
Geranium	Sunny	60-70°	Root cuttings in Aug. for winter bloom.	All the sun you can give them in winter.	Feb.-June.
Gloxinia**	Semi-sun (summer), sunny (winter)	65-75°	Plant tubers Oct.-Dec.; seeds, Jan.-Aug. Leaves root like African violet.	Lots of humidity; enough sun to make leaves hug top of pot.	Velvety blossoms Feb.-June.

OUTSTANDING INDOOR PLANTS

Plant	Amount of Light*	Best Temperature Range	When to Plant Seeds, Bulbs, Cuttings, etc.	Special Requirements	Bloom Time (If Any), Comments
Hibiscus, Chinese**	Sunny	65-75°	Cuttings any time.	Prune to keep in bounds; feed.	Year-round.
Oleander	Sunny	60-75°	Cuttings any time.	Prune. Summer out-doors. Lots of water.	Winter-spring.
Oxalis	Sunny	60-75°	Bulbs, spring or fall.		Year-round.
Peperomia** (many varieties)	Semi-shade	65-75°	Cuttings, divisions, any time.		Valuable foliage plants.
Philodendron** (many varieties)	Shady to semi-sun	65-75°	Cuttings will root any time.		Valuable foliage plants.
Pickaback plant (Tolmiea menziesi)	Semi-sun	65-75°	Young plantlets root any time.		Foliage is fresh, cheerful green.
Pink polka-dot plant (Hypoestes)	Semi-sun	65-75°	Roots easily from cuttings any time.	Pinch to induce bushiness.	Attractive foliage.
Rouge plant (Rivina humilis)	Sunny	60-75°	Plant seeds in spring or summer.	Pinch to induce bushiness.	Red berries over long period.
Rubber plant (Ficus elastica)	Semi-shade to sunny	60-75°	Increase by air-layering any time.		Large foliage plant for accent.
Shrimp plant (Beloperone guttata)	Semi-sun	55-79°	Cuttings root any time.	Prune to keep in bounds.	Blooms over long period of time.
Wax plant** (Hoya carnosa)	Semi-sun	60-75°	Root cuttings in water any time.	Blooms come from spurs at leaf joints, so don't pinch these.	Feb.-July.

*Figure amount of light as follows: SUNNY—at least 5 hrs. daily in winter (south window); SEMI-SUN—2 hrs. daily in winter (east or west window); SEMI-SHADE—dappled sunlight or strong light (unshaded north window); SHADY—no sun, but light strong enough to cast shadow.
**Plant will thrive under fluorescent lights.

Care of House Plants

CONTAINERS Have you tried the new plastic flowerpots? They are light-as-a-feather, easily scrubbed clean at repotting time, and they come in attractive decorator colors. Plants growing in plastic pots require less water than those in clay pots.

If you use clay pots, soak them overnight in water so they won't take moisture from newly potted plants. To clean old, dirty clay pots, put them in a bucket and pour boiling water over them. Add a half cup of bleach to the water and let stand for a few hours. After this soaking, it's easy to wash off the pots so they look like new.

If you like, you can use fancy containers that have no drainage holes. The best way is to grow a plant in a smaller clay pot, and place this inside the decorative container. If you grow a plant directly in a waterproof pot, put at least an inch of broken crockery, pebbles, or chunks of charcoal in the bottom. Charcoal is best since it helps keep the soil fresh.

SOIL MIXTURE There was a day when making a proper soil mixture for any particular plant was like trying to follow a complicated soufflé recipe. Today, complete water-soluble fertilizers for container-grown plants make all this soil mixing outdated.

It's the texture of the soil that's important. If the soil drains poorly and becomes waterlogged, plants won't survive. If the soil is too sandy and dries out quickly, becoming powdery despite all watering efforts, plants are sure to wither away. Every house plant we grow thrives in a spongy, humusy mixture composed of equal parts of garden loam, peat moss, and sand. If you have a pet soil recipe that makes plants thrive for you, then by all means stick to it.

FERTILIZING Set up a regular fertilizing program for your house plants. A water-soluble house-plant fertilizer is best. Follow the directions on the container. In general, these fertilizers are applied every two weeks to plants in active growth.

If a plant is inactive due to dormancy, disease, or insect attack, it should not be fertilized. Proper fertilization can produce large, healthy plants in small pots. It helps to make full-size leaves of brilliant colors. A fertilizer high in potash content helps to induce flowering, but sunlight plays the all-important role in flower production.

Don't apply fertilizer to a plant that is wilted as a result of being too dry. Water the plant well and then apply the fertilizer solution in a day or two.

REPOTTING When the soil in a pot becomes full of roots, the growth of the plant slows down. It's then time to transplant it. To remove the plant, put one hand across the top of the pot to hold the soil and turn the plant upside-down. Tap the rim of the pot on the edge of a table, and the ball of earth will come easily from the pot.

If the ball is not full of roots, it may not hold its form. Then you'll know that repotting isn't necessary, and you can put the plant back in the same container. Sometimes a plant slows its growth naturally before a dormancy period, or the slowing may indicate a lack of plant food or improper growing conditions.

If the soil is full of roots, and they form a sturdy root ball, repotting is in order. Pots are measured across the top. Select a pot ½ to 1 inch larger than the old one. Slip the plant inside, and place new soil around it, pushing in the soil lightly with your thumbs. Do not tamp it down or it will cake and drainage will be poor. Water well and set the plant in a cool, shaded place for a few days until it begins to show new growth. Then return it to its regular place in the window garden.

SELF-WATERING FLOWERPOTS CAN BE BOUGHT OR MADE

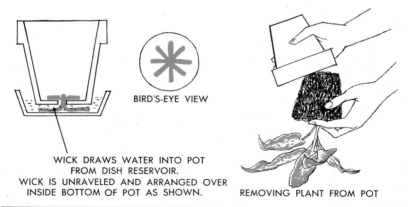

BIRD'S-EYE VIEW

WICK DRAWS WATER INTO POT
FROM DISH RESERVOIR.
WICK IS UNRAVELED AND ARRANGED OVER
INSIDE BOTTOM OF POT AS SHOWN.

REMOVING PLANT FROM POT

WATERING Use your eyes and fingers to determine if the soil is actually wet, nicely moist, or powdery dry. If it's dry, water thoroughly by setting the pot in a pan of water until moisture is evident at the surface. Or water from the top until water drains from the hole in the pot. If a pot of soil seems habitually too wet, watch for signs of rot. Soil that stays soggy wet prevents roots from functioning properly, and decay sets in.

Don't water with icy cold water! Use water at room temperature.

SUMMER CARE   All house plants (except the most delicate) bene-
fit from a summer spent outdoors in the shade of a tree, a shrub, or on a
porch. House plants should be protected from hot, dry winds. Large-
leaved plants, such as philodendron and angel-wing begonias, should
have protection from rain storms.

During the summer, repot any plants that need it. Continue fertilizing
plants in active growth. Watch for and spray insect infestations.

Several weeks before frost is expected, bring the plants back indoors.
They may lose some foliage as a result of the sudden change in humidity
and light. Moving from garden to porch to window garden lessens the
shock somewhat.

PROPAGATION   Most house plants that grow from a fibrous root
can be divided. Take cuttings from new growth that has hardened a
little. Root cuttings in a cutting box.

Fill the box with a 50-50 mixture of peat moss and sand, or peat and
vermiculite. Keep it moist and place where it will receive good light. Just
insert the cuttings (with labels so you'll know what's what) and when
roots are well formed, put the plants in individual pots. Keep the pots in
the cutting box for 2 to 3 days after transplanting, until the plants begin
to grow.

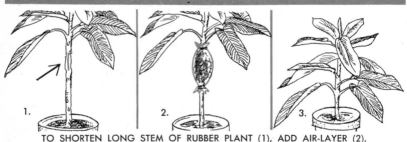

TO SHORTEN LONG STEM OF RUBBER PLANT (1), ADD AIR-LAYER (2).
WHEN ROOTS FORM IN AIR-LAYER, NEW PLANT CAN BE POTTED (3).

Some plants of a shrubby nature, such as the rubber plant, are propagated by making an air-layer, as follows: With a knife slit the stem about
a third of the way through. Wedge a piece of moist sphagnum moss into
the cut, then wrap a handful of the moss around the stem. Secure a
piece of polyethylene plastic around the moss. Make it airtight by tying
the top and bottom. When roots have a good start in the moss (up to 8
weeks or longer), sever the new plant from the old and pot it separately.

BEATING THE BUGS No matter how healthy your plant collection, sooner or later there are certain insects that may attack.

MEALYBUGS are cotton-like critters about ½ inch long. They dine on the undersides of foliage, in the crevices between leaves and stems, and around flower buds and new growth. Repeated applications of an aerosol house plant spray are effective against them. Coleus is the favorite of the mealybug. When the insect gets a foothold in coleus, better burn the plant.

SCALES are tiny sucking insects. They form what appears to be a tannish-brown, oblong spot on leaves and stems of plants with glossy foliage, such as begonia and amaryllis. If you look closely, you'll see the insects. For a bad infestation, use the aerosol spray. If there are only a few, flip them off with a knife and crush them.

APHIDS, which attack your roses and chrysanthemums outdoors, also like house plants. Aerosol spray is most effective against them.

THRIPS are tiny black, thread-like sucking insects that dine on the undersides of leaves, in flower buds, and on stems. They favor gloxinias and cause the stems and leaves to take on a rusty appearance, which finally becomes burned spots. Use aerosol spray weekly against them.

WHITE FLIES often attack cinerarias, flowering maples, fuchsias, and whatever else you grow. If you try to spray white flies, they will go away until you're through, then return. If the weather is warm enough, gently carry the infested plant outdoors, without disturbing the flies, and knock them off the plant with water from the hose.

CYCLAMEN MITES often attack African violets, causing new growth to be distorted. Treatments for cyclamen mites are dangerous, so it is better to burn the plant.

NEMATODES cause knots to form on roots. By the time their work shows up in the stunting of the top growth, the plant, soil, and pot should all be destroyed.

SPRINGTAILS are the little gray insects that hurry around so busily in pots of house plants. They're harmless.

MEALYBUGS

SCALES

APHID

CYCLAMEN MITE

SPRINGTAIL

Two Unusual Plants to Try

ROSARY VINE

THE ROSARY VINE Ceropegia is the botanical name of a delightful, easy-to-grow vine, more commonly known as rosary vine or hearts entwined. Ceropegias, tropical plants of the milkweed family, produce fleshy, heart-shaped leaves on a long, thread-like stem. The strange flowers come in the leaf axils. They are waxy, about two inches long, and quite indescribable. The vine requires only moist soil, a warm window sill, and semi-sun. As the stems mature, the leaves drop, and bead-like tubers form where the leaves grew. When the "beads" are pressed into warm, moist soil, they will grow into new plants.

THE VOODOO PLANT Also called snake palm and devil's tongue, this plant is a calla-lily relative known botanically as Hydrosme rivieri, a member of the arum family.

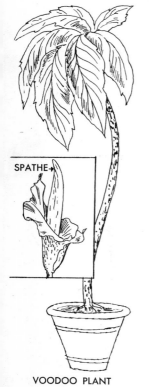

SPATHE→

VOODOO PLANT

The tubers of the voodoo plant can be potted in regular potting soil, which should be kept moist. Like its calla-lily relative, the plant thrives on lots of water and sunlight while it is in growth. In the spring the tubers send up bloom spikes. The giant reddish-black blossom is intriguing and has the smell of carrion. Out of the center of the calla-like bloom comes a spathe — a finger-like growth — hence the names snake palm and devil's tongue. If this spathe is cut out as soon as the bloom opens, the plant will not be so odorous.

After the plant blooms, its foliage arises into a magnificent fan-like umbrella. When the weather warms up, the voodoo is usually planted outdoors, in a part of the garden that is protected from strong winds. The foliage lasts until frost arrives. The tubers should then be dug up and stored in a mouse-proof place at a 50-degree temperature. Later in the winter the tubers can be potted again, and the cycle started anew.

House Plants in the News. Several members of the Gesneriad family, whose most famous member is the African violet, have made big news in indoor gardening. The newsmakers are:

Gloxinera. This plant is the result of a cross between a gloxinia and a rechsteineria. Gloxinias are known and admired by all indoor gardeners. Few have grown the rechsteineria, a plant that, like the gloxinia, grows from a tuber and requires warmth, some humidity, semi-sun, and a moist, spongy soil. The first gloxineras were produced by Peggie Schulz, a housewife-writer-photographer from Minneapolis, Minn. The drawing shows her "Rose Bells" gloxinera, which will thrive and bloom on any warm, semi-sunny window sill where other plants grow.

GLOXINERA

Double gloxinia. Gloxinia growers have long dreamed of a variety with double flowers. The first of these were introduced in 1958. In 1959 Bruce Thompson, an engineer for the Pennsylvania Railroad, received a Silver Medal from the International Flower Show for his perfected double gloxinias. They were the result of a seven-year hybridizing program carried on under fluorescent lights.

DOUBLE GLOXINIA

Flame-violet. This is the trade name of a handsome foliage plant, the Episcia. Episcias have become available only recently on a commercial basis. They come in a glorious array of leaf patterns, all of which are marked with silver, chocolate, pink, or other colors. Like strawberry plants, Episcias have stolons, or runners. When they receive enough warmth, light, and humidity, they produce bright clusters of flowers. With both handsome foliage and flowers, Episcias make a welcome addition to the indoor garden. The plant shown is Episcia reptans. It was drawn from a photograph of a plant grown in the north-facing window-sill garden of Olga Rolf Tiemann in Missouri.

FLAME-VIOLET

Success with Old Favorites

WHAT MAKES AFRICAN VIOLETS BLOOM? For best results with African violets, the following conditions are recommended:

SOIL: loose, porous, well-draining, with a pH of 6.5 to 7.5. If a test indicates that your soil is more acid than pH 6.0, try watering with lime-water instead of plain water. Dissolve ¼ teaspoon of hydrated lime in 1 tablespoon of water. Add this to about 10 quarts of water. Expect results after about 3 months.

FERTILIZER: 5-10-5, 13-26-13, or 15-30-15.

MOISTURE: warm, moisture-laden air is best. Kitchens and bathrooms usually contain the most humidity. Keep African violet soil moist, not drippy wet or powdery dry. Use room-temperature water.

LIGHT: semi-sun (about 2 hours daily in winter). African violets need some sunlight for bloom production. An east or west window is suitable during most of the year. If you live in the sunny Southwest, violets may bloom in your north windows.

THREE WAYS TO INCREASE AFRICAN VIOLETS

1. WITH KNIFE, WORK SIDE CROWN APART FROM MAIN PLANT, SEPARATE ROOTS, AND REPLANT CROWN. 2. ROOT LEAF BY SETTING ITS STEM AN INCH OR TWO DEEP IN SOIL. 3. ROOT LEAF IN WATER, USING WAXED PAPER TO SUPPORT STEM.

THE TOP 25 AFRICAN VIOLETS Twenty years ago there were a scant half-dozen different African violets. Today there are an estimated 3,500.

In a popularity poll conducted in 1958 by the 16,000-member African Violet Society of America, these were the African violet varieties that came out on top: White Madonna, Ohio Bountiful, Granger Garden's Blue Nocturne, Bud's Strike Me Pink, White Pride, Black Magic, White Pride Supreme, Pink Miracle, Double Pink Cloud, Ruffled Queen, T-V Vallinpink, Snow Prince, Pink Cheer, Dixie Moonbeam.

GIVING PLANT NEW START

SCRAWNY PLANT IS CUT BACK. NEW GROWTH IS THICKER, BUSHIER.

KEY TO GERANIUM CARE   To bloom indoors in the winter, geraniums must have all the sun you can possibly give them. An unshaded east or south window will usually provide enough light. A temperature range of 60 to 70 degrees is ideal. A fertilizer with a 15-30-15 ratio will enrich the soil and help the plants to bloom. Too much nitrogen will cause the plants to produce all foliage and no flowers.

Geraniums must be "pot-bound" to give good blooms. Be sure your pots are not too large.

POINSETTIAS AT CHRISTMAS   Have you ever coaxed a poinsettia to grow from one season to another, only to have it bloom months after Christmas, or perhaps not at all? Here's how you can avoid disappointment.

The blooming time of many plants is controlled by the amount of daylight they receive. Some plants require a "long day"—12-14 hours of daylight—in order to bloom. The fuchsia is an example.

Poinsettias are "short day" plants (as are chrysanthemums). Hence, as the short days before Christmas approach, the plant normally presents its cheerful display of red bracts (the true flowers are the little yellow parts at the center of the red bracts).

But if your poinsettia is in a room where the lights are on until 11 at night, you are providing a long day. Even regular, momentary bits of light at night serve to break the short day. So for Christmas bloom, see that your poinsettias are kept in a room where there is *no* light except daylight after the first of October.

POINSETTIA

Try Something Different

GARDEN WITHOUT SOIL For anyone who likes to experiment, growing plants without soil can be a fascinating pastime. One substitute for soil can be made by mixing equal parts of peat moss and perlite (an expanded lava rock) and by adding soluble fertilizers to provide plant food. Or you can buy a new commercial product called Styra-Soil, which is a colored synthetic soil, with plant food added.

Perennials can be grown in large flower pots, trees and shrubs in wooden tubs. In growing plants without soil, follow the same rules of temperature, light, etc., that ordinarily apply.

GROW MINIATURE TREES Growing artificially stunted trees, or Bonsai, is an old Japanese custom. Bonsai are tiny replicas of trees that would normally grow to a large size. They are dwarfed by trimming and pruning branches and roots and by confining the plants in small containers.

Anyone who is willing to invest a little time and effort can grow these miniature trees. In Japan, some are more than a century old and are passed on from generation to generation. No expensive equipment is needed. The trees themselves can be dug up anywhere or bought from nurseries. They can be grown in small trays or dishes.

Growing Bonsai can be an engrossing hobby, especially if you have any artistic talent. For the trees can be trained and shaped into works of art.

One of the best accounts of how to grow Bonsai is given in a special issue of *Plants and Gardens* magazine, available for $1 from Brooklyn Botanic Garden, 1000 Washington Ave., Brooklyn, N. Y.

MUGHO PINE

JAPANESE YEW

MAKE A TERRARIUM No matter where or how you live, you can have a successful terrarium—a glass bottle, bowl, or other glass container enclosing a garden of small plants.

To plant a terrarium, place some bits of charcoal in the bottom of the container and add 2 to 4 inches of a mixture of peat moss, sand, and good garden loam. A commercially prepared planter mix, such as Black Magic, available at the florist's or ten-cent store,

TERRARIUM

is equally suitable. Plant some cuttings and keep the soil moist. If you like, place a piece of glass over the top to conserve moisture. Set the terrarium on a window sill and you will have a bowlful of bright growing plants that take almost no time or care. If the top is covered, even dust will not settle on the plants in their private greenhouse.

We have two conversation-piece terrariums in our house. One is planted in a box-shaped former fish aquarium. The plants originally came from a woodland area we visited on our honeymoon. We picked up small cuttings and seedlings, and planted them in woodsy, rich soil with plenty of pebbles in the bottom to hold excess water. This wild, woodland garden has four ferns, a wild strawberry, a pippsissewa, a forget-me-not, and a selaginella. A piece of mountain laurel is planted in one corner.

Each fall we carefully scoop out the plants and the soil, divide and cut back the plants, and replant them. We keep this terrarium on an unheated sunporch until temperatures drop below 45°; then it goes to an east bedroom window where the temperature is seldom above 64° in the winter.

Our other terrarium is a large brandy snifter containing small plants from the tropics. These include a miniature caladium, three kinds of selaginella for ground cover, and a small fern. The scene-stealer in this planting is a miniature gloxinia. This little plant, small enough to grow in a thimble, produces lavender flowers all year.

We keep both terrariums in a well-lighted north window in the summer. In the winter, the brandy snifter sits near an east window.

GROW MUSHROOMS Want to raise mushrooms in your basement? Pre-planted mushroom trays are sold by the Luxor Company, Newark 3, N. J. All you do is water them, and they will produce mushrooms for your family.

Which Greenhouse for You? You can stretch your gardening season to a full 12 months with a greenhouse. It can be as simple as a $35 fixture that fits in your window. Or it can be as elaborate as a $750 greenhouse that stands in your garden.

Window greenhouses receive heat during winter from the room to which they are attached. They can be used all year for growing exotic plants, African violets, and foliage plants. In spring, seeds and cuttings can be started in them. In summer, they are hard to ventilate and may get too hot for the plants.

As for larger greenhouses, here are some tips to help you decide what might be best for you.

COVERING   Plastic-covered greenhouses are the answer for people who have big gardening ideas but small pocketbooks. A simple wooden frame covered with transparent sheet plastic becomes a satisfactory greenhouse. When heated in winter, it can be used to grow any plants desired. The plastic covering may have to be renewed every second or third year, but it is much less costly than glass.

Fiberglas greenhouses are worth considering. They cost about the same as glass greenhouses, but are unbreakable and lose heat very slowly.

FRAME   Aluminum-frame greenhouses have become popular with home gardeners. Though more expensive than wooden-frame types, they are easier to maintain, since they don't have to be painted and won't rot, warp, or decay. Their cost has now come down to the point where a small aluminum-frame greenhouse can be purchased for several hundred dollars. All are prefabricated for easy erection by the home handyman.

STYLES   The two basic styles of greenhouses are the lean-to and the even-span. The even-span is the type usually seen at nurseries. The lean-to type is attached to one side of a building, preferably the south side, where the greenhouse will get the most sunlight. If possible, an even-span greenhouse should run north and south.

Lean-to greenhouses are less expensive but not as roomy as the even-spans. When attached to a home, the lean-to type is easier and cheaper to heat. A doorway makes it possible to enter the greenhouse from the home without going outside. This is particularly convenient in bad weather.

HEATING AND VENTILATION   Heaters for greenhouses can be electric, oil, coal, or natural gas. Automatic ventilation and heating are almost mandatory if there is nobody to look at the temperature and regulate ventilators throughout the day. For the summer, there are now air conditioners for greenhouses.

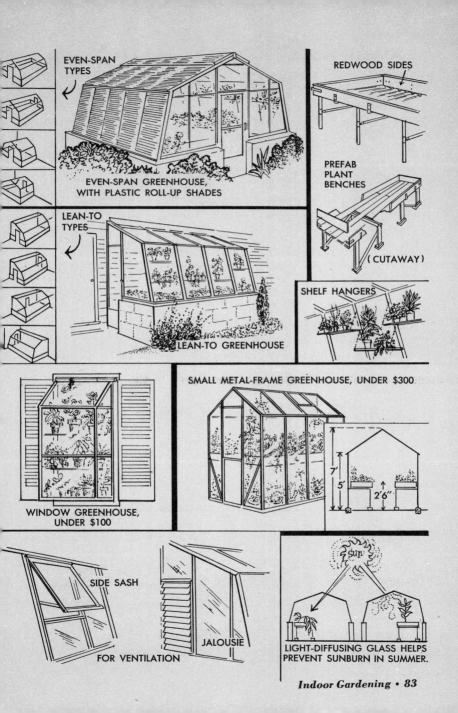

EVEN-SPAN TYPES

EVEN-SPAN GREENHOUSE,
WITH PLASTIC ROLL-UP SHADES

REDWOOD SIDES

PREFAB
PLANT
BENCHES

(CUTAWAY)

LEAN-TO TYPES

LEAN-TO GREENHOUSE

SHELF HANGERS

SMALL METAL-FRAME GREENHOUSE, UNDER $300

7'

5'

2'6"

WINDOW GREENHOUSE,
UNDER $100

SIDE SASH

JALOUSIE

FOR VENTILATION

Sun

LIGHT-DIFFUSING GLASS HELPS
PREVENT SUNBURN IN SUMMER.

Easier Outdoor Living

Editor of this section is one of America's leading specialists in outdoor living, John Burton Brimer. This artist-writer-traveler is author of the book, *Designs for Outdoor Living*. He is an editor of *Flower Grower* magazine, a contributor to other national magazines, and an outstanding lecturer.

The trend in the 1960s will be to more and more outdoor living. A man's grounds as well as his home will be his castle. More entertaining will be done out-of-doors—and more relaxing, too. Furniture, shelters, and equipment will be increasingly designed for this purpose. Whether you have an estate or a 50-foot lot, outdoor living will make your life more pleasant in the decade ahead.

Make the Most of Your Terrace. Outdoor living generally revolves around the terrace, which has become the outdoor living room of Americans. Obviously, the terrace should be as comfortable and pleasant as possible. To make it so, here are some things to think about when you are building or improving a terrace.

LOCATION   Place the terrace where it can be easily reached from the living room, the kitchen, or both. Or, if you prefer, make a self-contained terrace in a rear corner of the lot.

PAVING   A paved terrace drys quickly after storms, making it usable for most of the outdoor year. Paving also gives a stable footing for chairs and for foot traffic that would badly wear grass. Blacktop, brick, cement blocks, concrete, or stone are all good permanent paving materials. Gravel, tanbark, cinders, and other materials may be used for temporary surfacing.

COLORS   Dark colors absorb and retain heat. Heat collected on a hot day by a dark pavement may be given off late into the night. This is undesirable where nights are uncomfortably warm. While light colors reflect heat, they also reflect light, producing intolerable glare in sunlight. Medium-toned stone and colored concrete reflect and disperse some heat without making undue glare.

GOOD CONCRETE MIX

CEMENT

SAND

GRAVEL

Mix 1 part cement, 2 parts sand, 3 parts gravel with water for smooth concrete

SIZE AND SHAPE   Before building the terrace, set out the chairs and tables you plan to use on it. Rearrange the furniture for the most comfortable use. Consider what traffic lanes you must leave open.

Now stake out the outlines of your terrace. Outlining the area with a long garden hose will enable you to experiment with different shapes before the actual staking-out.

POINTS TO REMEMBER   Will nearby trees provide shade, or must you make a special provision for it? Perhaps you'll want a roof over part of the terrace to shelter your family and friends in case of a sudden shower and to protect your outdoor furniture. Will you be using the terrace on warm evenings? If so, think about lighting. These and other considerations are discussed in the pages that follow.

Concrete can be painted or dyed.

What Outdoor Furniture is Best? This is a question *you* can answer better than anyone else. You'll surely want outdoor furniture that is comfortable, since the terrace and garden are for your leisure-time pleasure. You'll also want pieces that can be easily moved for storage or for putting under cover when it storms, yet durable enough to last a number of seasons. Some furniture can be built in where it will be most useful. Built-in benches and seats are especially handy for parties.

Select furniture with an eye to beauty as well as practicality. After all, you'll be spending a lot of time outdoors, and handsome furniture can add to your pleasure. Many practical pieces will do nothing whatever to enhance the terrace. So don't be lured into buying "bargains" that you'll tire of and probably replace in a year or two. Choosing carefully now will save you money in the long run.

SHOPPING TIPS

Sturdy redwood furniture is easy to move when it has wheels. . . . *Iron furniture* is most permanent; iron tables often are equipped with umbrellas for shade. . . . *Aluminum folding chairs* are laced with or upholstered in quick-drying plastics to permit use soon after rains. . . . An *ottoman* makes a chair into a chaise longue. . . . *Circle chairs* of rattan on an iron frame are both comfortable and good looking. . . . *Large loose pillows,* kept in a stack, can be distributed for extra seating. . . . *Stacking chairs,* which fit one on top of the other, take little space when stored indoors for the winter or when the terrace must be quickly cleared for games. Their lightweight aluminum frames make handling easy. . . . A *folding metal table* can be stored in a very small space when not in use and sometimes comes in handy indoors. It can be carried in the car for use on picnics and on camping trips.

BUILT-IN FURNITURE

PERMANENT BENCHES offer aux-
iliary seating for lawn parties. Bases
of the benches can be made from
concrete blocks or from ceramic flue
tiles filled with concrete. Wooden
tops can be bolted into the concrete
before it hardens. Permanent tables
can be made in a similar way.

SEAT-WALLS, which are actually
retaining walls or walls of raised
plant beds, also offer many possibilities for additional seating. Built
of bricks, concrete blocks, concrete,
redwood planks, or any other durable material, they'll add to the
beauty of the terrace and grounds.
Loose pillows can be placed on the
seat walls to make them more comfortable.

LET-DOWN TABLE is particularly
useful on the small terrace, where
demountable or disappearing furniture is a must. The table, built
into the wall or into a fence beside
the terrace, can be lowered when
needed. If cleverly constructed, it
will blend with wall or fence and
won't be very noticeable when not
in use.

TREE SEAT can be built of concrete blocks or bricks around a tree,
leaving space through which the
tree can be watered. Wooden seat
is made fast by bolts set in mortar
between blocks. All wood used outdoors should be treated with liquid
wood preservative before it is
painted.

Outdoors—But Sheltered. The ideal outdoor terrace is one that is partly open to admit sunlight, partly covered to provide shade and storm protection, and perhaps is entirely screened to keep out insects.

Sometimes the roof of the house can be extended to cover part of the terrace. Even if it can be extended only a few feet, this will provide a cover under which furniture can be moved when a storm threatens.

Corrugated plastic roofs have become popular for use over terraces. They have the advantage of keeping out rain, yet allowing plenty of light to come through.

For cool shade on a hot summer afternoon, there is nothing like a tall, spreading tree. But in the absence of a tree—or a solid roof—there are other ways to provide shade. For instance, a few 2″ x 4″ posts will support a "roof" of trellis slats, over which annual or perennial vines can be grown. Even the slats alone will break the force of the sun's rays, furnishing a certain degree of shade. Roll-up bamboo blinds or slatted porch blinds can be attached to the sides of the framework to give protection against the late afternoon sun. The framework may also be screened if insects are a problem.

In constructing a screened-in outdoor shelter, use wide screening so that uprights and crosspieces can be spaced fairly far apart, thus keeping the view as unobstructed as possible.

FOR SHADE: TRAIN VINES
OVER AN OVERHEAD TRELLIS

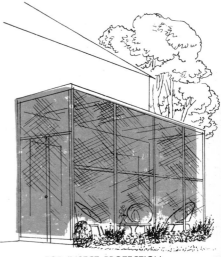

FOR INSECT PROTECTION:
BUILD A SCREENED SHELTER

Make Your Outdoor Day Longer. Either permanent or portable lighting fixtures will add immensely to the use you can make of your terrace. For best results, follow a few simple rules.

PLACEMENT   Before you put up permanent lights, try them in a number of locations to determine the most satisfactory arrangement. Try to conceal lamps so they won't be noticeable, night or day. Lamp housings painted a deep green, for example, will disappear into foliage.

BACKGROUND   Remember that light-colored walls and fences will reflect and diffuse light, thus extending the illuminated area. Cooking, eating, and work centers need brighter light.

WEATHERPROOF FIXTURES   Special plastic-covered feed wires to outlets and lamps can be buried without housing. But avoid burying them where you may be spading the garden later on. All lamps and outlets should be weatherproof fixtures designed for *outdoor use.*

LIGHTS ABOVE EYE LEVEL   Place these as high as possible—on house, poles, or trees—to give a wider spill of light and to attract insects upward, away from people. Insects killed by a lamp's heat will fall, so keep tables and chairs out from under lights.

LIGHTS BELOW EYE LEVEL   Mushroom-shaped lamps are recommended for low-level light. They use ordinary bulbs and will cast a small patch of light on steps, pools, etc. They may be set permanently or, if the stake-bottom type is used, can be moved from place to place.

INSECT KILLER   Electric ultraviolet lamps are made especially to attract and electrocute insects. They may be plugged in and moved to where you plan to sit. Yellow bulbs are good for places where you do not want to attract insects.

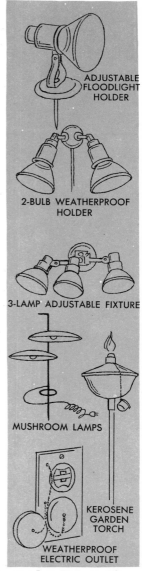

ADJUSTABLE FLOODLIGHT HOLDER

2-BULB WEATHERPROOF HOLDER

3-LAMP ADJUSTABLE FIXTURE

MUSHROOM LAMPS

KEROSENE GARDEN TORCH

WEATHERPROOF ELECTRIC OUTLET

Fun for the Children. There's a lot to be said for setting aside a play area for the children. They'll be pleased to have a part of the yard they can call their own, and you'll be pleased if this helps keep them out of your flowerbed. But don't be too optimistic about that!

The play area should be fairly level and partly shaded. If the children are small, it should be located where it can be easily seen from the house, preferably the kitchen. You may want to enclose the area with a temporary fence. Consider paving part of it for the use of tricycles, wagons, and wheeled toys. As the children get older, you may want to screen the play area from the rest of the yard with shrubs and other plantings.

To help the kids have fun, you may want to consider some of the following games and equipment:

A PLAYGROUND SET of swings, trapeze, and rings—with perhaps a basketball board and even a shower attached—gives endless fun.

A CLIMBING GYM built of steel pipes or of wood and metal gives children plenty of exercise.

TETHER BALL—a tennis ball in a net suspended by a rope fastened to the top of a 10-foot-high pole—is played with table tennis paddles.

OTHER GAMES that lend themselves to back-yard playing by young and old include badminton, croquet, shuffleboard, horseshoes, and table tennis.

PLASTIC SANDBOXES now available can become small pools after children have outgrown them. The water connection for a fountain and drainage pipes can be installed now and plugged until they're needed in a few years.

A TENT in the back yard is always fun for children. Let them sleep outdoors, cook on an outdoor grill, and pretend they are miles from home—until they need you.

HOW TO BUILD A PLAYHOUSE   Children will spend endless hours "keeping house" if they have a playhouse of their own. One can be made as follows:

(1) For a foundation, put in and level four concrete piers or concrete blocks set on concrete. (2) Use 2″ x 4″ boards for framing, set 16″ apart (measured from center to center) for floors. Space and locate boards as in sketch. Two opposite sides of frame should measure 8′ in width; the other two opposite sides should measure 8′ minus twice the thickness of the plywood to be used for the exterior. (3) Cut plywood in pattern shown and nail to framing. Plywood cut from door opening is used for door; smaller pieces and other plywood are used for floor. Door is kept rigid by 1″ x 2″ framing, which also supports hinges. (4) Use scrap boards or plywood for roof, covering it with roofing paper or asphalt shingles. (5) Install regular windows or do-it-yourself aluminum storm sash with mullions painted on the glass. Shutters can be real or can be plywood imitations with short strips of wood glued or screwed to wood to represent crossbars.

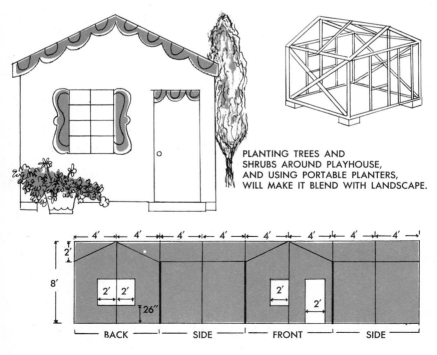

PLANTING TREES AND SHRUBS AROUND PLAYHOUSE, AND USING PORTABLE PLANTERS, WILL MAKE IT BLEND WITH LANDSCAPE.

BACK — SIDE — FRONT — SIDE

Outdoor Cooking. Strange and wonderful things happen when a meal is cooked and eaten outdoors. Appetites sharpen, a relaxed holiday spirit prevails, and the food smells and tastes better—or so it seems. It's no wonder that the back-yard barbecue is becoming an American custom.

EQUIPMENT The type of grill you use is largely a matter of personal preference. A permanent fireplace is nice, though time-consuming to build. Portable grills that use charcoal or electricity are convenient. They can be wheeled into position, shifted to protect the fire from the wind, put under shelter in case of a sudden rain, and stored indoors for the winter. Some people use a gasoline camp stove for back-yard cooking.

Here is a list of other equipment you may want:

Basic Items	Optional Items
Long-handled fork, spoon, turner	*Bellows to blow fire*
Long-handled frying pan	*Electric charcoal starter*
Hinged broiler	*Clam and lobster steamers*
Carving board (for steaks, etc.)	*Dutch oven (outdoor iron one)*
Asbestos gloves	*Ice buckets (up to 1 gal. capacity)*
Pot holders	*Griddle (for pancakes, etc.)*
Long-handled tongs	*Hibachi (Japanese charcoal stove*
Long-handled basting brush	*good for small groups, children)*

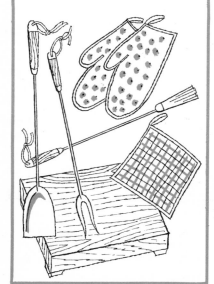

COOKING SUGGESTIONS Organize your menu to do as much as possible in advance. Make up cooky sheets of hamburgers. Lay them in tiers separated by waxed paper and store them in the refrigerator. Have as many fix-it-yourself foods as you can manage.

Hero Sandwiches

Hero sandwiches are over-sized, over-stuffed, and delicious. Each is made with a whole loaf of bread filled with a variety of foods. A meal in itself, it serves several people.

To make a Hero, slice a long loaf of French or Italian bread lengthwise once and toast. Spread with garlic or onion butter (½ cup butter with ½-1 tsp. garlic or onion powder and 2 tbs. fresh finely chopped parsley, thoroughly mixed). Wrap in foil and heat over grill, turning frequently.

For a hamburger filling, shape meat a little larger than the bread used. (Cheese, onion, tomato paste, or anything you prefer can be mixed with the meat.) Grill meat until done, then flip onto bread prepared as above. Spread with ketchup or chili sauce, add layers of sliced onions, tomato, pepper, or whatever you like, including cheese. Cover with other piece of bread and slice into portions for serving.

For steak Heros, cover broiled steak with layers of sliced vegetables — carrot strips, cauliflower, mushrooms, etc. Top with mayonnaise and water cress.

Barbecued Meats

Make a basic barbecue sauce as follows: In a skillet, brown 1 chopped onion and 1 chopped green pepper in 2 tbs. corn oil. Add 1 large can tomatoes, 2 cloves garlic (or ½-1 tsp. garlic powder), 6 cloves, 1 small bay leaf, 2 tsps. celery seed. Simmer slowly until vegetables are soft (30 min.); then strain and add 2 tsps. butter, ½ tsp. salt and coarse black pepper to taste, a dash of cayenne, 2 tbs. brown sugar, a dash of Tabasco sauce, 2 tbs. Worcestershire sauce, 4 tbs. wine vinegar (or 4 tbs. lemon juice). Heat until very warm to blend ingredients. Use either hot or cold.

Some cooking uses are:

Grilled or Roast Chicken. Brush barbecue sauce and butter alternately on bird as it cooks.

Broilers. Split broilers. Brush all over with barbecue sauce. Broil cut side down 20 minutes, turn, and broil 15-20 minutes longer. Baste often with sauce.

Cold sliced turkey. Brush sauce on slices, heat in hinged broiler over fire. Brush on sauce each time you turn slice.

Hamburgers, franks, and other meats. Use sauce to taste.

Housing Your Pets. Every dog has his day outdoors, but he needs a house at night. Cats should be kept indoors at night. Experts tell us that they may die of exposure or possibly suffer frozen ears in zero weather. A box with a soft blanket or cushion, placed in a corner of the garage or cellar, will provide an adequate place to sleep.

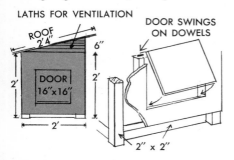

LATHS FOR VENTILATION
ROOF 2'4"
DOOR SWINGS ON DOWELS
6"
2'
DOOR 16"x16"
2'
2'
2" x 2"

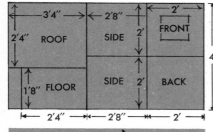

3'4" — 2'8" — 2'
2'4" ROOF SIDE 2' FRONT
4'
1'8" FLOOR SIDE 2' BACK
2'4" — 2'8" — 2'

A DOG HOUSE that's easy to make has a simple 2" x 2" frame, covered with ½" outdoor plywood. A swinging door allows the dog to enter at will, yet keeps out drafts. Pattern sketch shows how a 4' x 8' plywood sheet is cut to make house. Designed for a medium-sized dog, this plan may be adapted for larger or smaller animals by varying dimensions. Set house on 2" x 4"s to keep floor from contact with cold, wet ground.

A RABBIT HUTCH can be made as shown. Framing is 2" x 2"s; door frames, 1" x 2"s. Sides are 1" x 2" wire screening. Floor is made of perforated aluminum to allow for drainage but to hold litter. Roof is one piece of outdoor plywood pitched for drainage. Nest boxes should be 8" x 16" x 16" or larger. Remove them at weaning time, when young need floor space. Place hutch where there is light and air, but no draft. Keep it well off the ground.

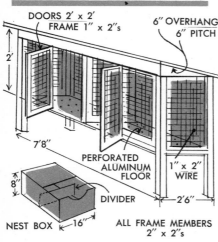

DOORS 2' x 2'
FRAME 1" x 2"s
6" OVERHANG
6" PITCH
2'
7'8"
PERFORATED ALUMINUM FLOOR
1" x 2" WIRE
8"
DIVIDER
2'6"
NEST BOX 16"
ALL FRAME MEMBERS 2" x 2"s

IN-AND-OUT DOORWAY for pets, made of flexible plastic, can be installed in house, garage, or doghouse. Designed to keep out cold, rain, and insects, it comes in sizes to fit animals from cats to great Danes. Write: Turen, Inc., 50 Beaver Park, Danvers, Mass.

Attracting Birds to Your Yard. Birds and gardens belong together. Every gardener has a soft spot in his heart for birds. Though they may eat a few seeds, they'll make up for it by destroying many insect pests. Bird watching is an absorbing hobby, particularly for children. To create interest among your children, post color pictures of birds on their bedroom walls. Children quickly learn to identify birds that visit your backyard.

Many kinds of birds can be attracted even to a small yard if you provide for some of their basic needs.

FOOD   Any plants that have berries or fruit will attract birds. The following plants, varieties of which can be grown in most parts of the country, are popular with birds: pines, oaks, cedars, dogwoods, birches, blackberries, wild cherries, and grapes.

If you build or buy a bird feeder and keep it well stocked with food, you can entice many birds to stay around all winter. For the most enjoyment, locate the feeder where it can be easily seen from a window. Birds will eat bread crumbs and many other table scraps. Wild-bird-seed mixtures and sunflower seeds, available at pet shops and other stores, will attract a great variety of birds.

Beef suet is a favorite food of chickadees, nuthatches, woodpeckers, and others. Suet should be tied or fastened in some way to trees or feeders so larger birds don't carry it off.

WATER   Birds like shallow water both for bathing and drinking. A bird bath should slope gradually from the edge and have a rather rough surface so that it's not slippery when wet.

SHELTER   In winter most birds like cozy evergreens in which to hide from the wind, snow, and rain. Spruce, cedar, and pine make good shelters for chickadees and other birds that remain in colder climates for the winter.

In the spring, birds need a sheltered spot for nesting. Some prefer natural nesting places in trees and bushes, while others will accept a man-made shelter. Dense shrubbery or evergreens such as junipers are attractive to some birds. Others, like the Baltimore oriole, prefer large deciduous trees. A few trees and plenty of thick shrubs will bring the most birds.

If you want to build a nesting house or shelter, make it simple. Birds don't go for bright paint and fancy trimmings. Robins, for example, like to nest on a simple shelf with a roof over it.

For more details on how to attract birds, write: National Audubon Society, 1130 Fifth Ave., New York, N. Y.

How About a Swimming Pool? Today there are so many kinds of pools in so wide a range of prices that the question is not "Can we have a pool?" but merely, "What kind?" Anyone who wants a pool is likely to find one suited to his pocketbook.

Pools range from the inexpensive portable types to costly custom-built tiled pools that are lighted for night bathing. Pools are now being built in a variety of materials—poured concrete, metal, tile-on-concrete, asphalt, and even prefabricated glass-fiber construction, particularly good in mild climates. Plastic-lined pools are increasing.

For a small back yard and a limited budget, a portable pool may be the answer. These pools range in depth from 18 to 48 inches. They come in many diameters. Portable pools generally consist of metal frames with plastic liners. You fill them with a garden hose and drain them by siphoning. Collapsed and folded up, they may be stored during the winter in the garage, the attic, or the basement.

BEFORE YOU BUY Permanent pools are a big investment. Before deciding on one, it's wise to talk with pool owners in your area. Ask them whether they are satisfied with their pools, who built them, what their problems have been, and how much they spend for annual maintenance and repairs.

Check building codes and local and state laws to see what is prohibited and required regarding pools. Some states require pool owners to carry insurance and to fence a pool—always a good idea. Deeds may contain restrictive covenants, so be sure to check them.

Make sure you have an adequate water supply (some localities restrict the use of water during the summer) and that the water is cheap enough to use. Check what electricity will be needed for filter and heating mechanisms. Make certain that adequate drainage is available.

WHERE TO PLACE POOL Locate the pool in full sunlight where there are no overhanging trees to shade it or to drop leaves in it. Don't expect to place the pool where water, sewer, gas, electric, or phone lines are buried underground. Don't build on filled land, and remember that ledge rock, hardpan, or underground springs run up costs.

OTHER TIPS Periodic draining and scrubbing to remove scum, algae, and foreign matter will keep the pool clean and hygienic. Elevating the pool and the paved area about 8 to 16 inches will help prevent grass clippings and leaves from blowing in and fouling the water.

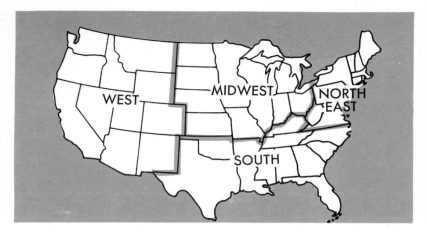

Regional Gardening Calendars

In this section, gardeners will find information on what to do and when to do it for the entire year. Since gardening activities vary somewhat with climate, there is a separate gardening calendar for each of four major regions—the Midwest, the Northeast, the South, and the West. The calendars cover spring, summer, fall, and winter activities. Each regional section is edited by an outstanding horticultural writer.

For the most part, these are brief reminders. Most of the activities are covered in detail elsewhere in the book. A check of the index will give the page number.

Of vital importance to gardeners are the frost maps on pages 98-101. These give an idea of when the last spring frost and first fall frost may be expected in various areas. There will, of course, be variations in these dates from year to year. Also, within an area, frost dates will vary with elevation, nearness to water, etc. So use the maps as a general guide to be supplemented with local weather information.

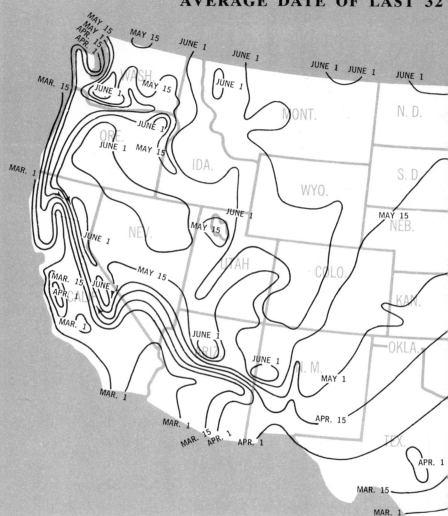

AVERAGE DATE OF LAST 32°

MAY 15
MAY 15
APR. 15
APR. 1
MAY 15
MAY 15
JUNE 1
JUNE 1
JUNE 1
JUNE 1
JUNE 1
MAR. 15
JUNE 1
MAY 15
WASH.
JUNE 1
MONT.
N. D.
JUNE 1
JUNE 1
MAY 15
ORE.
JUNE 1
MAY 15
IDA.
S. D
MAR. 1
WYO.
JUNE 1
MAY 15
NEB.
JUNE 1
NEV.
MAY 15
UTAH
COLO.
MAR. 15
MAY 15
APR. 1
JUNE 1
CAL.
KAN.
MAR. 1
JUNE 1
JUNE 1
OKLA.
JUNE 1
N. M.
MAY 1
MAR. 1
APR. 15
MAR. 1
MAR. 15
APR. 1
TEX.
APR. 1
APR. 1
MAR. 15
MAR. 1

RAPID CHANGES IN ELEVATION IN THE MOUNTAINS
PRECLUDE ACCURATE DRAWING OF ISOLINES.

U. S. DEPARTMENT OF COMMERCE, WEATHER BUREAU

TEMPERATURE IN SPRING

AVERAGE DATE OF FIRST 32

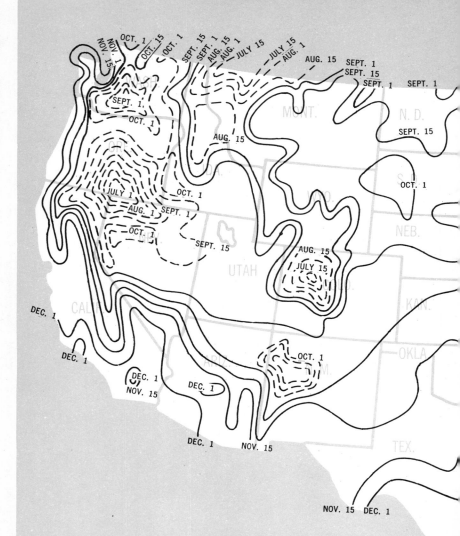

RAPID CHANGES IN ELEVATION IN THE MOUNTAINS
PRECLUDE ACCURATE DRAWING OF ISOLINES.

U. S. DEPARTMENT OF COMMERCE, WEATHER BUREAU

EMPERATURE IN FALL

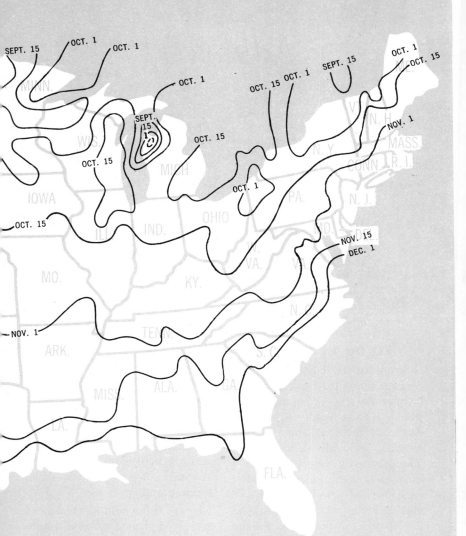

SEPT. 15 OCT. 1 OCT. 1 OCT. 1 OCT. 15 OCT. 1 SEPT. 15 OCT. 1 OCT. 15

SEPT. 15 OCT. 15 OCT. 15 OCT. 1 NOV. 1 NOV. 15 DEC. 1 OCT. 15 NOV. 1

MINN WIS MICH N.Y. VT N.H. MASS CONN R.I N.J PA OHIO IND ILL IOWA MO KY W. VA VA MD N.C S.C GA TENN ARK MISS ALA LA FLA

Midwest

Dr. Milton Carleton, editor of this section, is a widely known leader in Men's Garden Club of America, a pioneer in many garden practices, and author of such books as *Bulbs, New Ways to Kill Weeds,* and *Your Lawn.* He is Midwest editor of *Flower Grower* magazine, a contributor to many national magazines, and research director of Vaughan Seed Co.

• •

TO DO IN SPRING

●SNOW MOLD. If there are grayish or tan-pink patches all over the lawn when the snow melts, the trouble is snow mold, a fungus disease that flourishes only in cold weather, especially under snow. The grass will come back as long as its roots aren't killed, but other fungi may also find conditions favorable for growth. So it's a good idea to rake out dead grass and apply a turf fungicide. If you see no traces of green grass in two weeks, reseed the patches.

●SOIL. If soil was not turned over last fall, get this done as early as possible, but avoid packing soil by working it when too wet.

●JUNIPERS. Before warm weather comes, cut away the brown balls that form on Junipers—the resting stage of the rust that also affects apple, crabapple, and hawthorn trees.

●SEEDLINGS. Don't start seedlings indoors too early. For hardy flowers and vegetables, figure back eight weeks from date of last killing frost; for tender plants, eight weeks back from last light frost. Use the new peat-and-fiber pots to avoid shock of transplanting.

●LAWN. If the weather is cool and wet, spring-planted lawns will have a good chance to succeed. Ordinarily, August is the best month to start lawns in the Midwest.

•Roses. Don't be in too much of a hurry to uncover roses. Gradually remove covering so they will still have a little protection at time of last killing frost.

As soon as rose branches show new "breaks," start a regular spray program, using a mixture that is both a fungicide and an insecticide. The new Phaltan is the top-rated control for blackspot.

•Spraying. If dormant sprays were not applied during the winter, do this on a day when air temperatures will stay above 40 degrees for several hours, but before leaves show a trace of green.

•Nursery stock. Start planting nursery stock as soon as soil is workable. A wet spring is particularly good for planting.

•Compost. Any time is fine for starting a compost heap, but the trash from the spring cleanup should yield plenty of material to use. Add some fertilizer to the pile to help speed rotting of leaves.

•Early planting. Hardy annuals and vegetables can be seeded as soon as the soil can be worked. They often are just as early in coming up as transplants and usually are less subject to disease.

•Peonies and tulips. As peonies and tulips break through the soil, spray shoots with Captan, Phaltan, or Fermate. This controls Botrytis blight.

•Evergreens. When new shoots on evergreens are about two inches long, cut off half of the new growth. This encourages bushiness.

• Fall colors. Spring is the time to plant for fall colors. One of the most spectacular fall plants is the dwarf burning bush. In fall it is a vivid rosy carmine without a trace of green or yellow. It's a slow grower, so the earlier it can be started, the better.

As a companion, try Rhus canadensis, the fragrant sumach. It grows from 3 to 4 feet high. Its autumn color is a mixture of copper, red, orange, and yellow. Plant it in front of the burning bush.

TO DO IN SUMMER

● VEGETABLES. Keep planting lettuce, beets, carrots, and endive until July 1 to 15. First planting of Chinese cabbage should go in July 1, no earlier.

Make final plantings in the vegetable garden — leaf lettuce, radishes, and turnips—on August 15.

● FLOWER PLANTING. For good fall bloom, plant seeds of cosmos, calendula, and zinnias from July 1 to 15.

In July and August, plant madonna lilies, bearded irises, Oriental poppies, mertensia, and hardy amaryllis. They are dormant at this time.

● TULIPS. If you dig tulips for the summer, be sure bulbs are stored where the temperature is above 55 degrees but below 75 degrees.

● LILACS. Remove lilac flowers as soon as they fade, but *don't* cut away the two buds at the base of the flower stem. Next year's blooms will come from these.

● DELPHINIUMS. Start new delphiniums from seed sown August 15.

● APHIDS. Car stained with sticky drip from trees? Aphids are at work. They do little damage to trees, but a good spray man can eliminate them quickly.

● LAWN. Fungus diseases start browning out lawns in June. To kill fungi and aid recovery, apply a complete turf fungicide such as Kromad or Formula Z.

● SHRUBS. Increase shrubs by making soft-wood cuttings from mid-June until mid-July. Stuck in sand or vermiculite, the cuttings will root in a few weeks.

● CHRYSANTHEMUMS. Pinch out the tops of hardy chrysanthemums twice before July 1, not later, to produce bushier plants and more flowers.

● PLANTING EXPERIMENT. If you like to experiment, try planting a not-too-hardy shrub whose range is usually more southerly. Some gardeners have had good luck doing this by giving special protection the first couple of winters, then letting the plant go on its own.

An example is the Metasequoia, a relative of the giant redwood and introduced from China. It is being grown successfully in Michigan by caging it with chicken wire the first two or three winters. The cage is filled with dried leaves about the time of the first frost and is kept in place until the daffodils bloom in spring.

●WEEDS. For crabgrass control, apply Sodar on July 15 and August 15. Use 2,4-D to catch this year's crop of broad-leaved weed seedlings.

●DAY LILIES. If your perennial border needs color in midsummer, try perking it up with day lilies (Hemerocallis). These will be blooming at your flower dealer's, and you can take them home and plant them when in full bloom.

GARDEN VISITS. Visit outstanding gardens this summer, not only to see beautiful displays of flowers, but to learn about new plants to try at home. Some Midwest favorites:

Longwood Gardens, Kennett Sq., Pa. This is the most important garden in America and one of the finest in the world.

Morton Arboretum, Lisle, Ill. (20 miles west of Chicago).

McCormick Memorial Gardens, Cantigny, Wheaton, Ill. (3 miles west of Morton Arboretum).

Missouri Botanical Gardens, 2315 Tower Grove Ave., St. Louis, Mo.

Beal-Garfield Botanic Garden, Michigan State University, East Lansing, Mich.

Park of Roses, 4048 Roselea Place, Columbus, Ohio.

Kingwood Center, Mansfield, Ohio.

GROWING PANSIES

Middle of August is the best time to sow pansy seed over most of the Midwest. Pansies do best in a light, loose workable soil, so use all the well-rotted compost or other organic matter you can spare. Be sure drainage is good. Pansy seeds need lots of moisture but will drown if soil is waterlogged.

Shade the seedbed with laths spaced 1½ inches apart on a frame, or with burlap. Sow the seed on the surface; give it a light covering of vermiculite, sand, or peat.

Seed should germinate in 2 weeks. When plants have 2 or 3 leaves, transplant them in a coldframe, spacing them 6 by 6 inches, for winter. If any flowers open, pick them off.

TO DO IN FALL

● LAWN. September care determines the quality of next spring's lawn. If fall weather is dry, be sure to water the lawn often and well.

Keep mowing the lawn as long as growth continues, usually long after the first frost. Be sure to pick up clippings.

If snow mold turned your lawn gray last spring, now is the time to fight the fungus that did the damage. Apply Formula Z, Kromad, or Tersan right after the first killing frost.

● BULB STORAGE. Don't wait until the last minute to provide storage for tender bulbs and winter vegetables. Check your cellar storage now, so you will be prepared if an early frost comes.

● PEONIES AND SMALL BULBS. September 15 is the time to plant peonies. The little bulbs—crocuses, snowdrops, glories-of-the-snow, and narcissi—should all be planted in September as soon as the bulbs arrive at the nursery.

● LILIES OF THE VALLEY. Mid-September is a good time to remake lily-of-the-valley beds. Divide plants into single crowns and replant only the strongest, most vigorous of these. This plant is a heavy feeder, so don't spare the fertilizer.

● HYACINTHS AND TULIPS. Hyacinths and tulips are best left to be planted in October or early November, but watch the forecasts so you don't delay too long and find the soil frozen.

● GLADS AND DAHLIAS. Dig glads and dahlias before heavy freezes occur. A light frost won't hurt them.

● WINTER RYE. Plant winter rye (the variety Rosen is good) in any vacant spots in the vegetable garden. It makes wonderful green manure when turned under in spring.

● EVERGREENS. September is the best month of the year to transplant evergreens. Keep watering them, unless the weather is wet. Mulch roots the first winter.

All evergreens should go into the winter with the soil thoroughly moist, but not so wet that air is driven out. Where the soil is dry, it may be necessary to water them during winter thaws.

● LILIES. Lily bulbs aren't available until very late, so dig holes for them now, storing the soil indoors until the bulbs arrive. Set bulbs in frozen holes and cover with stored soil.

● **HOUSE PLANTS.** Bring in house plants left outside for the summer, but spray them first to prevent insect pests from coming in with them.

● **PUMPKINS AND SQUASHES.** Gather pumpkins and squashes before they are touched by frost, but as late as possible to allow them to ripen fully.

● **LEAVES.** Never burn a leaf. If you don't compost leaves, dig them into the soil of the vegetable garden or shrubbery border.

● **HERBS.** Dig up a few herb plants and pot them for winter use. Chives and parsley are particularly easy to grow on a window sill.

● **FOUR-O'CLOCKS.** Old roots of four-o'clocks can be dug and stored like dahlias. They will make bigger plants next year than plants grown from seed. Keep them away from children—both roots and seeds are poisonous.

● **IRIS.** Dutch, English, and Spanish iris should not be planted until just before freezing weather; otherwise they make top growth that is easily killed.

● **ROSES.** Did mice get into your roses last winter? To keep mice away, dust the ground with Toxaphene just before applying the winter covering.

HOW LATE CAN YOU PLANT TULIPS?

We've pried off a frozen crust of soil the last week in December, planted leftover tulip bulbs, and had the finest show of color in years the following spring.

The one thing to be sure of is that the bulbs are good. If you buy them at a bargain, ask for permission to cut a bulb or two. By late November the flower bud may be visible when the bulb is split from top to bottom. If the anthers are a bright clear yellow, the bulb is in good shape; if they are turning brown, it may survive; if black or very dark brown, chances are the bulb will die.

TO DO IN WINTER

• **LAWN WEEDS.** During a winter thaw, apply new forms of calcium arsenate, sold under several trade names, to pre-kill the seeds of Poa annua (annual bluegrass), crabgrass, knotweed, and chickweed. A lawn 100 per cent free of crabgrass is possible if you do the job right.

Avoid using the lawn as a short cut. Even when the ground is frozen, foot traffic can wear out turf rapidly.

• **PRUNING.** Bare limbs give trees and shrubs no secrets to hide. This is the time to do corrective pruning. Shape up lopsided specimens. Cut away branches that cross or rub. But don't trim away flowering wood on shrubs that flower in the spring (forsythia, lilac, mock orange, etc.).

• **LAWN.** When snow is off the ground, but the lawn is still frozen, you can apply the first fertilizer of the year. If you use one of the new mixed ureaform fertilizers, one application will do the job for all year.

• **ROOTSTOCK.** Check stored dahlia, glad, and other rootstock. If sprouting, they're too warm; if mildewing, too damp; if shriveling, not wet enough. Discard any that show rot.

GROWING TUBEROUS BEGONIAS

Tuberous begonias should be started in March to have them blooming next summer. So order them as soon as the new catalogues are out.

Set them on top of a mixture of half sand and half peat moss, kept damp. Barely press the tuber into the surface. When a mass of roots has formed, and a strong pink shoot has emerged from the top, put in a 4-inch pot. After danger of frost, set them out of doors.

(Begonias need special handling in hot Midwestern summers. Give them rich soil, high in decayed organic matter. Place them where they will get plenty of light without direct sun. Best place is where they are touched by sun before 10 and after 4).

Northeast

Frederick F. Rockwell and his wife, Esther, are the co-editors of this section. They have probably written more gardening books—25 at last count—and articles than any other writer or writing team. Mr. Rockwell is senior editor of *Flower Grower* magazine. The Rockwells live in Orleans, Mass.

● ●

TO DO IN SPRING

● NEW FLOWER BEDS. Take advantage of warm, sunny days for constructing new flower beds or borders. Use plenty of peat moss or compost.

● FERTILIZING. Fertilize roses, lawn, perennials. If the spring is cold and wet, 1 pound of nitrate of soda added to each 10 pounds of fertilizer is helpful.

● PERENNIALS. To get more and better blooms, divide perennials, discarding old woody centers. This is a good job for rainy days. Label them—most are replanted in fall.

● EARLY PLANTING. As soon as the ground can be worked, plant roses; also sow hardy vegetable seeds such as spinach, radishes, onions, lettuce, beets, carrots. Set out cabbage plants.

● LAWN. Two most important jobs for March or early April are fertilizing and rolling the lawn (with a light roller). Use a high-nitrogen fertilizer. Roll while the ground is still moist, but *not* muddy.

If the weather is cool and wet, the grass will grow fast. Cut it frequently, setting the mower's cutting bar fairly high.

● APRIL-MAY PLANTING. In late April or early May, as the danger of late frost grows less, sow seeds of tender vegetables (corn, beans, etc.) and of annuals such as larkspur, asters, and calendulas.

- **WEEDS.** As soon as weeds start, do a thorough job of cultivating and weeding. Here, "a stitch in time" saves more than nine.

- **ROSES.** In April, as growth starts, reprune roses to live wood; also begin a regular spraying program to control black spot, other diseases, and pests.

- **FROST PROTECTION.** Spring weather in the Northeast is very tricky. So it's wise to provide frost protection for tender vegetables planted in early May. Do this by putting hot kaps or plastic covers over the young plants. The covers help protect the plants from pests, too.

TO DO IN SUMMER

- **EARLY SUMMER PLANTING.** On a wet day, after the last killing frost is due, set out tomatoes, peppers, eggplants; also tender flowers such as begonias and caladiums.

- **ROSES.** Prune rambler-type roses after flowering, cutting back to the ground the canes that have flowered.

- **CHRYSANTHEMUMS.** Pinch back chrysanthemums for the last time, and fertilize them generously.

- **PERENNIALS.** Most important flower garden operation for June or early July is to start seeds of perennials and biennials to grow plants for next year's garden. Prepare seedbed in a frame or some spot that can be protected from stray animals and heavy, beating rains. Add ample peat moss or other humus to soil. Keep soil moist by frequent light sprinkling or by fine mist until seeds germinate—anywhere from a few days to two or three weeks. As soon as seedlings begin to crowd one another, thin them out until they are 1 to 2 inches apart or transplant them.

- **DEAD BLOOMS.** Cut off at ground level the dead blooms of delphinium, columbine, and lupine to encourage new growth for late flowering.

- **IRISES AND POPPIES.** In July, divide and transplant bearded irises and Oriental poppies.

- **AUGUST PLANTING.** Early in August, sow seeds of pansies, English daisies, and forget-me-nots.

- **EVERGREENS.** August is the best time to transplant evergreens. Use plenty of peat moss in the planting holes, and keep evergreens well watered for at least 6 weeks.

- **CUTTINGS.** Make cuttings of geranium, ageratum, lantana, heliotrope, and fuchsia for potted plants that will bloom indoors in winter.

• EVERLASTINGS. Cut and dry everlastings for winter bouquets and arrangements. It is usually sufficient to hang such flowers as celosia and strawflowers upside down in a dry room—the attic, if possible.

• BULBS. After spring-flowering bulbs bloom, fertilize them liberally and water them if necessary. Purpose is to keep foliage growing vigorously, so there will be good bloom *next* spring.

TO DO IN FALL

• LAWN. Late August through September is the best time to make a new lawn or remake an old one. Grass starts vigorously in cool, wet weather, whereas few weeds do.

• TREES AND SHRUBS. Late September and October—before the ground freezes—is an ideal time for planting trees and shrubs.

• FROST PROTECTION. New plastic materials are ideal for protecting dahlias, chrysanthemums, tomatoes, and other tender plants from first frosts. Try them.

• WINTER RYE. As vegetable crops are harvested, sow winter rye to be turned under in spring as "green manure."

• MULCHING. Summer is a good time for mulching—the application of vegetable matter in a blanket on top of the soil around or in between plants. Of the many materials used for this purpose, one of the best is half-decomposed organic matter. Spread it evenly, 2 to 3 inches thick, in vegetable and flower garden. Spread it 4 to 5 inches deep around trees and shrubs to conserve moisture and prevent weeds.

• COMPOST. Gather fallen leaves, debris, and weeds (if free from ripe seeds) for the compost heap. Any clean vegetable matter that will decay is fine. *Burn* all diseased or pest-infested materials.

• BULB PLANTING. Plant daffodils, tulips, and other spring-flowering bulbs at least 4 weeks before the ground freezes. Plant deep—at least 6 inches, preferably 10 inches for large bulbs.

• BULB STORAGE. As soon as tender summer-flowering bulbs, corms, and tubers—dahlias, cannas, tuberous begonias, etc.—are blackened by frost, take them up and keep them under cover. When tops dry up, cut them off and store bulbs and tubers in a cool but frostproof place.

• LATE WATERING. Drain all outdoor water systems before the first freeze. But see that shrubs and trees are well watered into November, so they will not lack moisture in winter.

● **New trees.** Greatest danger to trees planted in the fall is from the high and drying winds of winter. To prevent loosening or breaking of newly formed roots, brace trees in *three* directions before ground freezes hard. Use heavy wire (covered with a short length of hose where it touches the bark) or plastic clothesline with a wire core. Rope will stretch.

● **Winter blooms.** If you start now, it is easy to have hyacinths, tulips, and daffodils blooming indoors from Christmas to Easter. Simply pot them in good loam, water thoroughly, and then sink the pots to their rims in the soil in a coldframe (or in a trench a foot deep in a well-drained spot in the garden). Cover them to ground level with damp peat moss. In 6 to 8 weeks, when pots are filled with roots, bring them indoors.

TO DO IN WINTER

● **Tools.** Store away all tools, hose, and outdoor furniture before the first snow falls.

● **Mulching.** Do a complete job of mulching for winter. Roses will need extra protection. Mound 5 or 6 inches of soil over them before applying mulch.

● **Evergreens.** Prune evergreens just before Christmas. The trimmings make ideal holiday decorations.

● **Pruning.** After the turn of the year, watch for warm, sunny days in which to prune trees and shrubs.

● **Planning.** Make plans—preferably to scale—for any new gardens, flower borders, and tree or shrub plantings.

● **Bulbs.** Carefully inspect any flower bulbs or tubers that were stored for winter. If they have shriveled, pack them in slightly moist peat moss. Discard any that show rot.

● **Sweet peas.** As soon as the ground thaws, plant sweet peas in a trench 6 inches deep. As the plants grow, gradually fill in the trench with soil.

● **Catalogues.** Send for an assortment of seed and nursery catalogues. They contain a wealth of helpful garden information. Most of them are free.

● **New plants.** Order seeds, bulbs, and shrubs in plenty of time for *early* spring delivery.

South

Charles J. Hudson, Jr., editor of this section, is widely known for his book, *Hudson's Southern Gardening*. Past president of Men's Garden Club of America, he currently is general manager of Hasting's Garden Center in Atlanta, Georgia. He is a prolific writer and broadcaster on garden subjects.

● ●

TO DO IN SPRING

● LAWN CARE. Beware of loading lawn soils with high-nitrogen fertilizers only. They cause a lush, tender growth that can be hurt when hot summer weather arrives. Use complete fertilizers for best lawn growth.

● PERENNIALS. Ideal time for planting and transplanting perennials is in early spring just as new growth begins to show.

● IRISES. Feed irises with superphosphate to develop strong-stemmed blooms. As new growth develops, start borer-control spraying with DDT.

● SUMMER BLOOMS. Plant cannas, gladioli, callas, and dahlias for summer and fall blooms. Be sure soils are well drained for all but callas.

● CALADIUMS. Fancy-leaved caladiums are extremely popular for their vari-colored foliage and for their ability to flourish in shady places. Since caladiums are sensitive to cold, wet soils, start tubers indoors, in flats of peat moss, early in the spring. Growing plants will then be ready to be set out after the danger of frost is past.

● ROSES. March 1 is the annual pruning time for roses in the mid-South. Dormant plants are just beginning to put on new growth. Prune a week or two earlier in areas south of a line extending from

Charlotte through Greenville, Atlanta, Birmingham, Corinth, and Little Rock. North of this line, prune a week or two later.

●CAMELLIAS AND AZALEAS. Feed camellias and azaleas just after they have finished blooming. Use a special azalea and camellia fertilizer. Rake mulch away from the plants, apply the fertilizer, water it into the soil, and then replace the mulch.

●FLOWERING SHRUBS. Prune early flowering deciduous shrubs immediately after flowering.

●NEW LAWNS. Springtime is lawn planting season in the South. Cool-season grasses (mixtures, Kentucky bluegrass, and fescues) are planted in early spring in the upper South. In the deep South, wait till mid-April or later to start planting warm-season grasses (Bermuda, Zoysia, centipede, St. Augustine) from seeds and sod.

●ANNUALS. Start planting annual flower seeds after danger of frost is past.

●IN-BLOOM PLANTING. Gardeners are usually advised not to plant shrubs and perennials while plants are in full bloom. One exception to this rule is that azaleas, thrift, and candytuft are planted in early spring when the plants are loaded with flowers. Most gardeners would rather select these plants while they are in bloom. Magnolias and dogwoods also react well to early spring planting. They seem to do better than they do when planted during the coldest winter months.

●DRAINAGE. Wet spring weather is apt to leave garden soils soggy and sour—too much so for many garden plants. Check poorly drained spots and provide drainage by tiling or by the addition of gravel or sand. This is especially necessary for plants that grow from bulbs or tubers. Azaleas and camellias also do not thrive in poorly drained soils.

TO DO IN SUMMER

● BULBS. If the summer is wet and hot, your bulb plantings may suffer. To be on the safe side it would be wise to dig established plantings of tulips, daffodils, hyacinths, etc. Dry them off and store in a cool, dry basement until planting time in the fall.

●TOMATOES. Tomatoes are the favorite garden vegetable in the South—despite blight, wilt, and nematodes. Blossom-end rot, a white-purple fungus, is a summertime problem that comes with changeable weather conditions. Check this trouble by adding lime to the soil at planting time or by spraying plants with calcium chloride as fruit begins to develop.

● WEEDS. Weed-killer sprays make the control problem an easy one for lawns, but it takes hoeing and pulling to keep them out of the garden.

●BORERS. Borers are bad pests on dogwood, oak, and pine trees. Prevent infestations by spraying tree trunks with DDT or 20 per cent Lindane.

●AZALEAS AND CAMELLIAS. The second feeding of azaleas and camellias comes in the first half of June, as plants begin to set flower buds for next season.

● BEDDING PLANTS. Bedding plants are much in demand in early summer, when gardeners like to buy partially grown plants to develop early flowering in the garden. These plants bloom about a month ahead of ones started from seed.

● LAWN. In the deep South, lawns consist basically of hot-weather grasses that make their maximum growth during the hot summer months. So the time to plant your lawn is after the weather warms up. Select a lawn grass according to its tolerance to sun and shade, its texture, and its soil requirements. Bermuda grass likes full sun; centipede grass, sun to part shade; Zoysia and carpet grass, sun to medium heavy shade; St. Augustine grass, up to very heavy shade.

Summer grasses now popular are Tiffine and Tiflawn Bermudas, Emerald Zoysia, and centipede. These can be planted from sprigs, plugs, or solid sod, the latter mostly for steep banks.

● ROSES. Did you miss planting your roses during the dormant season in winter? It's not too late to do it even in June or early July, if you use plants grown in containers. You can set them out while they are in full bloom without any setbacks. It's like transplanting a geranium from a pot.

TO DO IN FALL

● BULBS. Fall bulb planting is the big garden activity, except in the deep South. Good drainage is essential for successful bulb culture, especially when fall weather is quite wet. Planting season starts in early September and runs through December.

● AUTUMN COLORS. Our southern mountains are a mecca for lovers of fall color, as hardwood trees display almost every hue in the rainbow when frosty nights approach. If fall weather is wet, colors will be especially brilliant. So plan to make a trip to the Cumberland, Blue Ridge, Great Smoky, or Ozark mountains.

● PEST CONTROL. It is too hot in summer to spray azaleas, hollies, and camellias for tea-scale control, so do this important chore in early fall before freezing weather sets in. Use oil sprays.

● LAWN. Fall lawn seeding is important to gardeners in the upper South, where cool-weather grasses thrive. Fescues do better when planted in fall rather than in spring. Get these grasses well developed before cold weather sets in. September planting is best; October, second best. In other sections of the South, during the same months, summer lawn grasses are overplanted with rye grass to produce green lawns all winter.

● FLOWER SHOWS. Fall is a time for dahlia and chrysanthemum shows. Some of the South's best dahlias are on display in the tri-city area of Atlanta, Birmingham, and Chattanooga in late September and early October. Mum shows are held a little later, around early November.

● CAMELLIAS. The camellia parade of blooms starts in September when the sasanquas lead off. Early varieties of japonicas soon follow to give us a colorful fall season. Sasanquas are well suited for hedges, specimen plantings, foundation plantings, and for espalier displays.

● PERENNIALS. Dig, divide, and replant old perennials in early fall so newly set plants can have the advantage of fall rains to become firmly established before cold weather sets in.

HOW TO GROW CAMELLIAS

Fall is a good time to plant camellias. They are rather easy to grow if you observe these few definite requirements:

1. Camellias like an acid soil rich in humus. This can be supplied by additions of peat moss.

2. Camellias give best color when in semi-shade. Plant them in the shade of pine trees or in shaded borders.

3. Camellias are very fussy about being planted too deeply. Set the top of the earth ball surrounding the roots 1½ to 2 inches *above* the soil level. This will allow for settling. Where soils are apt to be poorly drained at certain seasons, set the earth ball higher and protect exposed root tops with good mulches of pine straw.

In very sandy soils, plants can be kept from settling too much by setting the base of the earth ball on a central mound of soil that has not been dug or pulverized. Too deep planting or settling usually results in plants dying back.

TO DO IN WINTER

● MULCHING. Azaleas, gardenias, and pittosporum may need special protection during harsh winters. Persistently cold weather causes bark to split on stems. Mulch high around plants with pinestraw.

● ROSES. Protect roses in the upper South by hilling up soil around bases of plants.

● LAWN. In cold winters, hardy, cool-season grasses thrive. Fescues and bluegrass will provide good color throughout the winter in all but the middle and lower South, where rye grass provides green winter lawns.

● BULBS. Dutch bulb planting continues through December. December and January are best planting times for refrigerated tulips in the lower South.

● CAMELLIAS. Protect midwinter-blooming camellias against cold, drying winds by erecting a wind screen around each plant. Place four stakes around the plant and fasten burlap or plastic sheeting on the stakes to enclose the bushes. Leave top open for good air circulation.

Since camellias are in full bloom from November to March, visit at least one camellia show to acquaint yourself with the many excellent varieties suitable for greenhouse and garden culture.

● DRAINAGE. During a wet winter, check drainage of garden soils. Poor drainage can be damaging to bulbs and perennials.

● SPRAYING. Spray fruit trees, roses, and dogwoods with a dormant spray of liquid lime sulfur. It's a good protection against spring and summer disease infestations.

● LAWN WEEDS. Chickweed, Poa annua (annual bluegrass), and wild onions thrive in cold, wet weather. Keep lawns free of these pests by using special weed-killer sprays.

● VEGETABLES. Have fresh vegetables from your garden this winter. Plant English peas, onion sets, cabbages, turnips, mustard, beets, and kale.

● PRUNING AND PLANTING. Prune established fruit trees during their dormant period in the winter. This is also the time to plant fruit trees, as well as other trees and shrubs.

● DWARF FRUIT TREES. Plant dwarf fruit trees in home garden areas where space is at a premium. They are wonderful producers.

● ROSES. Plant roses from mid-November to early March. North Florida and Gulf Coast gardeners prefer November planting, but planting time in other sections of the South varies according to weather and soil conditions. Most gardeners prefer to set plants with the bud unions at or just below ground level.

AIR-LAYERING

Air-layering is one of the surest and easiest ways of rooting plant cuttings. And you can now get easy-to-use air-layering kits that enable you to produce large plants in a very short time.

Simply make a cut in a branch of any plant, shrub, or tree, and attach air-layer. Leave on for 2 to 8 weeks. No watering or attention is necessary. Then remove air-layer, and you find the branch has roots. Cut off and plant. A handy

air-layering kit is made by Horticultural Supply, Box 325, Stuart, Fla.

West

Richard D. Westcott, editor of this section, is a widely known horticulturist and garden writer throughout the West. He is general manager of Paul J. Howard's California Flowerland in Los Angeles. He contributes regularly to *Popular Gardening* magazine and is active in such groups as the National Shade Tree Conference, American Association of Nurserymen, and Southern California Turf Grass Council.

TO DO IN SPRING

● CRAB GRASS. Attack crab grass *before* it emerges in spring by applying calcium arsenate to the soil. Calcium arsenate will kill the seed as it sprouts, but will not injure lawn grasses—or even crab grass after it has sprouted.

In dry form, the chemical can be mixed with fertilizer and applied with a spreader. Since it remains effective for at least a year, sprouting seeds will be killed throughout the season.

● WATER. Although spring rains will be of great help, be sure to supply extra water to newly planted roses, fruit trees, etc.

● TALL FLOWERS. Stake your dahlias, delphiniums, gladioli, and other tall flowers to prevent winds and rains from toppling them over.

● VEGETABLES. Set out tomato plants and sow corn, beans, and other warm-weather vegetable seed in April.

● SPRAYING. Spray or dust tomato plants regularly with a combination insecticide-fungicide before trouble starts.

● FERTILIZING. Start a year-round fertilizing program for lawn and garden now—before new growth starts.

● GARDENING SCHEDULE. Don't let spring rains delay your planting, fertilizing, or spraying until it is suddenly too late.

TO DO IN SUMMER

●WATERING. If the weather is hot and dry, extra watering will be your principal job during the summer.

Irrigate fruit trees thoroughly after crops have been harvested—and once a month thereafter until leaves drop in fall. Run water slowly over a wide area around trees and shrubs, long enough to penetrate to deepest roots.

●MULCHING. Renew mulches around azaleas, camellias, rhododendrons, roses, and flower beds.

●LAWN. Feed lawn, using fertilizer with an insecticide added to control worms, grubs, beetles.

●INSECTICIDES. Spray or dust frequently to control insects, especially red spiders, whose numbers increase rapidly in warm weather.

●CHRYSANTHEMUMS. Cut back chrysanthemum plants early in July, then keep them in lush growth with fertilizer and water.

●DAHLIAS. Cut dahlia blooms with long stems to induce low branching and more long-stemmed flowers.

●SEEDS TO SOW. Seeds of perennials for bloom next spring and of annuals for winter bloom in warm areas should be sown now in shaded flats or boxes.

●ROSES. To keep rose bushes healthy during hot weather, apply fertilizer once a month and water them, thoroughly and deeply, at least once a week. A thick mulch of organic material will protect surface roots from drying out too fast. Combination sprays or dusts that control mildew, black spot, rust, and spider mites should be used at first sign of trouble. Clip off faded blooms before seed pods form.

VINES FOR SHADE

For color, screening, and shade in summer, plant fast-growing annual vines to cover arbors, porches, and fences. Grow them from seed planted in early June, or buy plants already started in pots at nurseries.

For variety, choose morning-glory vines in blue, red, or white. The Australian pea vine has lilac-pink clusters of flowers. Mina lobata, or Spanish Shawl, is a luxurious grower, with a profusion of bright red and orange flowers. To cover a tall structure, the Kudzu vine will grow to 30 feet in one season.

TO DO IN FALL

● WATERING. Continue to irrigate until fall rains have brought a total of several inches to your locality.

● GROUND COVER. Plant hillsides and banks with ground-cover plants, so that fall rains can aid in getting roots established enough to prevent erosion by winter rains.

● CUTTINGS. Make cuttings from tip growth of geraniums, heliotrope, fuchsia, lantana, and carnations.

● DAHLIAS. Dig dahlias when tops have died down. Store the clumps above ground, protecting them from drying and freezing.

● ROSES. Fertilize roses to produce a fall crop of long-stemmed buds for cutting.

● BULBS. Order spring-flowering bulbs early—to get the best selection—for planting in October and November. A warm, wet soil will rot ranunculus bulbs, so these may have to be held until November. If the weather is mild, it may be late November or early December before it is cool enough to plant tulips. (They will do a lot

TUBEROUS BEGONIAS

If you have the opportunity, take a trip to the tuberous begonia farms around Santa Cruz, on the coast south of San Francisco. Acres of these gorgeous flowers, in bloom from June to October, are in some ways more thrilling than the tulip fields of Holland.

You will see why these California strains are such prized garden flowers all along the coast, where they thrive, and why avid begonia fans grow them in pots and shaded beds in warmer areas, where they require somewhat more attention.

You can get begonia plants already growing in pots at nurseries for transplanting in your garden. An overhead misty spray will help keep them in best blooming condition. A mixture of peat moss, leaf mold, and sand is the best growing mixture for them, whether they are in pots or in solid beds.

better if you keep the bulbs in the refrigerator for several weeks before planting.)

● FLOWER SHOWS. Look for dates of flower shows featuring displays of chrysanthemums, roses, and dahlias.

• MUMS. Buy a pot of mums that are full of blossoms. Many nurseries produce mums in a great variety of colors and types. After they have bloomed, you can keep them for use as propagation stock next spring.

• PESTS. If the weather is warm, you will need to be diligent with your pest-control program.

• ANNUALS. Pull out annuals that have finished blooming. Spade up and fertilize soil for bulbs and for winter-flowering or spring-flowering plants.

• GRADING. Check the surface grade of your garden. Fill in low spots or provide underground drains to carry off excess water.

TO DO IN WINTER

• SOIL. Cultivate all open areas so rains will soak in and build up the deep soil moisture that has been depleted during past dry seasons.

• CATALOGUES. Study nursery and seed catalogues for varieties of roses, fruit trees, shrubs, flowers, and vegetables best suited to your garden.

• PLANTING. Plant bare-root roses, fruit and ornamental trees, and shrubs.

• SEEDS. Start seeds of petunia, verbena, ageratum, and lobelia in flats for transplanting to garden for early blooms.

• SWEET PEAS. Sow a row of sweet peas, first inoculating them with a commercial bacteria culture. Cover them with a light mulch for protection during the first few weeks.

• GLADIOLUS. Plant gladiolus bulbs at monthly intervals for a long season of blooms.

• BULBS. Bulbs of tulips, daffodils, hyacinths, lilies, ranunculus, and anemones can still be planted in January.

• FRUIT TREES. Prune fruit trees and protect larger cuts with pruning compound.

• ROSES. Prune roses in late January, in southern California and Arizona, but not until February or March in colder regions.

• SPRAYING. Control overwintering pests and diseases on fruit trees, roses, and some ornamental shrubs with dormant spray in January. Repeat just before leaves appear.

• CAMELLIAS. Select your camellias while they are in bloom; this is the best time to transplant.

DYE YOUR LAWN GREEN FOR WINTER?

If you are going to plant a new lawn, get it started before the heavy rains come. Older lawns should receive a liberal application of fertilizer in September, followed by lighter feedings at monthly intervals, to keep them green through the winter.

Many lawns in southern California, Arizona, and New Mexico are composed of Bermuda grass or Zoysia. These are warm-weather grasses and turn brown in late fall and in winter. Overseeding with annual rye grass or Highland bent grass will produce a green winter turf.

Another way to have a green lawn in winter is to spray on a green dye after a final mowing in the fall. The dye is a special one that will not wash off and will remain green until new spring growth takes over. Hardly anyone suspects it, but this dye is what makes the playing field in the Los Angeles Coliseum look so lush and green in spite of the beating it takes.

FROST PROTECTION

In all parts of the West some plants are grown that are on the borderline of being too tender for normal winters. Soft growth and tender new shoots produced in mild winter weather by plants that are usually quite hardy may sometimes be nipped by a frosty night or two.

When a freeze is forecast, use fir boughs, palm fronds, corn stalks, or cloth draped over stakes for emergency protection of tropical plants or evergreens that may be in new growth or in bloom. If some plants are damaged, don't cut them back until you can see where new growth will start. The dead stems and foliage offer some protection to the live wood.

Garden Tools and Machines

Editor of this section is William L. Meachem, associate editor of *Flower Grower,* the Home Garden Magazine. He also edits *The Garden Dealer Guide* and is the author of *An Easy Guide to African Violets.* A specialist in garden equipment, he has been connected with horticultural publications for the past 12 years.

One of the things that makes gardening so interesting is the tremendous assortment of tools, machines, and gadgets you have to work with. You can spend $15 or $1,500 on garden equipment, as you wish. Actually, you don't need elaborate equipment to have a beautiful garden and grounds. But the right tool will help you get a job done easier and faster. The following pages give you the facts you need to make an intelligent choice.

A Hoe for Every Purpose. A hoe isn't just a hoe any more. Look at the array of different hoes in catalogues or garden stores and you can find one for almost every type of plant grown. The old-fashioned hoe and narrow-bladed cousin—the floral hoe—are most popular for home flower and vegetable gardens.

A SCUFFLE HOE—pushed back and forth just beneath the soil's surface —cuts weeds off at the crowns. It doesn't go deep, takes less energy for weeding, and is ideal for working around shallow-rooted plants such as rhododendrons and azaleas.

FORKED CULTIVATORS can be pulled through the soil just as cultivators are pulled behind a tractor. Or they can be used in a chopping fashion like a hoe. Most useful type is the "potato hook," which is a small version of the old tool used by farmers to hoe potatoes out of the ground.

A WHEEL HOE is fine for working around vegetables and flowers grown in rows. Behind its one large wheel are the cultivating tines. It requires a little more muscle power to push than a scuffle hoe, but does a good job and is fast.

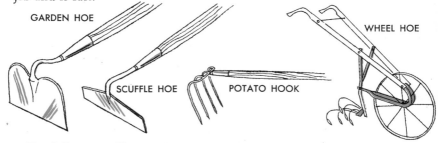

GARDEN HOE

WHEEL HOE

SCUFFLE HOE   POTATO HOOK

Push-button Gardening. The pressurized cans used for spraying paint and for shaving cream and toothpaste have invaded the gardening field.

Insect sprays in push-button cans are available for indoor plants and for such outdoor plants as roses. (Don't use household insect sprays on your plants.) When using a push-button insect spray, hold the can at least 18 inches from the plant so that the propelling gas has a chance to escape into the atmosphere. These sprays are best for touch-up spraying —use a sprayer or duster for the bulk of pest control.

Also available in push-button cans are leaf-shining spray for indoor foliage plants; poison-ivy killers; tree-wound dressing; and root-inducing chemicals for cuttings. These may be expensive when compared to the cost of the same amount of material bought for use in a sprayer, but the convenience often makes them worthwhile.

Basic Tools
for the Gardener

GARDEN HOSE ON REEL

WATERING

START WITH THESE	ADD THESE LATER
Watering can	Oscillating lawn
Garden hose (50 ft.)	sprinkler
Adjustable hose nozzle	Hose reel
Hose-type sprinkler	
Soil soaker	

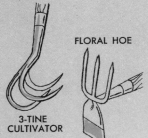

FLORAL HOE

3-TINE CULTIVATOR

CULTIVATING

START WITH THESE	ADD THESE LATER
Pronged cultivators	Wheel hoe
(long- and	Additional cultivators
short-handled)	
Floral hoe	
Scuffle hoe	

SHOVEL

SPADING FORK

SOIL WORKING

START WITH THESE	ADD THESE LATER
Spade	Tractor
Spading fork	Long-handled shovel
Shovel (D-handle)	Transplanting
Steel rake	(narrow) spade
Trowel	Woman's shovel and
	spade
	Bulb planter

LAWN

START WITH THESE
Mower
Broom lawn rake
Hand trimming shears
Hand edger

ADD THESE LATER
Lawn sweeper
Fertilizer spreader
Wheel or power
  edger

BROOM RAKE

PRUNING

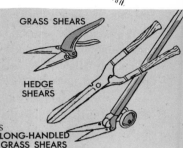

GRASS SHEARS

START WITH THESE
Hand hedge shears
Large pruning shears
Knife
Flower-cutting shears
Sickle

ADD THESE LATER
Lopping shears
  (two-handed)
Additional hand
  pruning shears
Electric hedge shears

HEDGE
SHEARS

LONG-HANDLED
GRASS SHEARS

SPRAYING

START WITH THESE
Hand sprayer
Plunger duster
Aerosol sprays

ADD THESE LATER
Pressure sprayer
Rotary duster
Hose-end sprayer

easy Sprayer

OTHER ITEMS

START WITH THESE
Stakes and labels
Plastic plant ties
Ball of twine
Garden gloves
Galvanized pail
Flower pots
Fertilizers
Insecticides

ADD THESE LATER
Coldframe or green-
  house
Seed flats
Garden cart or
  wheelbarrow
Carrier for hand tools

Which Sprinkler for Your Garden? Lawn sprinklers vary in price from 98 cents to more than $20. But how much you pay for a sprinkler is of little importance. If it will put the right amount of water on the lawn, it is a satisfactory sprinkler.

A PERFORATED HOSE SPRINKLER looks like a plastic garden hose with many tiny holes in it. Turn on the water, and you have a fine sprinkling all along its length. It waters a long narrow strip and can even turn corners. Relatively inexpensive, it is effective if left on long enough.

A STATIONARY SPRINKLER usually waters in a circular pattern. There are no moving parts to get clogged, but it will only do a small area, and often the fall of water is heavier in some spots than others. It is inexpensive, but must be moved often.

A ROTATING SPRINKLER has either one or two arms that revolve. It will cover a fairly large circular area evenly with a good amount of water.

AN OSCILLATING SPRINKLER has a single arched arm that swings back and forth. Most of these sprinklers can be regulated to cover various-size areas, if water pressure is adequate. Water pattern is rectangular. The sprinkler can water right up to a sidewalk or building without wetting it. This is the most expensive sprinkler. Prices range from $6 for a small one to $22 for the largest.

AN UNDERGROUND SPRINKLING SYSTEM is fine if there is enough need for watering to warrant the expense. Do-it-yourself installation kits are available, but check your local water department for any restrictive regulations before buying.

A GOOD HOSE is, of course, a must. Plastic is least expensive, and the reinforced kinds will last many years. Some are even guaranteed for 10 years. When not using hose, always shut off water at the faucet.

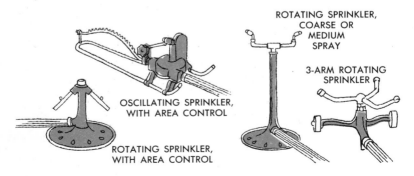

OSCILLATING SPRINKLER, WITH AREA CONTROL

ROTATING SPRINKLER, WITH AREA CONTROL

ROTATING SPRINKLER, COARSE OR MEDIUM SPRAY

3-ARM ROTATING SPRINKLER

Guns for Your Insect War. A regular program of spraying or dusting every two weeks will do wonders in keeping plants free of pests.

Spray or dust, which is better? Each has its advantages, and it's up to you to decide which you prefer. You may get better coverage of leaves with a spray, but when dusting you don't have to carry the weight of water through the garden.

Spraying can be done at almost any time of the day. Dusting is done only when there is no wind. Early morning, when the dew is still on the leaves, is the best time to dust. The moisture holds the material on the leaves. Usually a good spray job gives better coverage and controls insects better than dusting.

PUMP SPRAYER

DUSTER

HOSE-END SPRAYER

SPRAYERS. These come in many sizes, ranging from the simple pump type to large electric- or gasoline-powered models. When buying a sprayer, remember that a bigger one won't have to be filled as often.

A practical sprayer for average garden use is a pressure type with a capacity of 3 to 4 gallons. Pressure is built up in the tank by pumping. Spray is released through a hand-grip nozzle. New models have tanks on wheels. A handle used to push the tank through the garden is also used for pumping. These models are easier to move about and much easier to pump up.

Hose-end sprayers are attached to the end of the hose like a nozzle. A glass jar contains concentrated spray. As water passes through the sprayer, spray is siphoned out of the jar and mixed with the water in the correct dilution. One real advantage is that you can reach the tops of trees with the spray—that is, if your water pressure gives you that much reach. A deflector on the nozzle makes a fan spray for garden use.

DUSTERS. Small pump or rotary dusters are excellent for garden use. The pump type gives a puff of dust when the plunger is depressed. The rotary type gives a continuous cloud of dust. Dusters usually hold a limited amount of dust and have to be refilled often.

Is a Rotary or Reel Mower Better? The No. 1 garden tool is a power lawn mower. Power mowers have about relegated the hand mower to the antique shop. About 3 million power mowers are sold each year in the U.S.

The rotary mower is most popular and least expensive. Some 80 per cent of all power mowers sold are of this type. Cutting is done by a spinning blade beneath a metal housing.

Reel mowers are big brothers of the old hand mowers. Grass is sheared as it gets caught between a base blade and revolving reel blades. All power reel mowers are self-propelled, while some rotaries have to be pushed.

ROTARY VS. REEL. Which is better? This depends on conditions. For cutting rough grass with some weeds, rotaries are better, since they will cut tougher grass and small weed stalks. If the rotary blade is not sharp, however, the tips of grass stalks will be torn and will eventually turn brown. Rotary mowers can be set to cut very high—up to 3 inches—and will trim close to buildings, trees, and walls.

Reel mowers cut each blade of grass cleanly. So there will be no browning at the tip, unless the machine is not adjusted correctly. Reel mowers are usually preferred on better lawns, since they can be set to cut low for a "putting green" finish. New "trimmer" models of reel mowers will trim to within a half inch of walls and buildings.

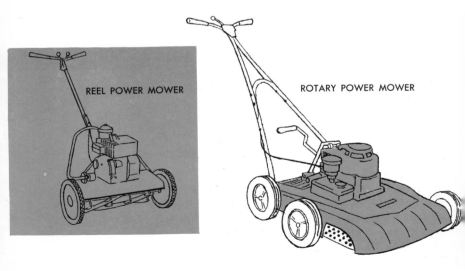

REEL POWER MOWER

ROTARY POWER MOWER

How LARGE A MOWER? Size of mowers is based on the width of the swath they cut. For smaller lawns, look for easy maneuverability rather than size. For large lawns, size is important, since an extra 2 or 3 inches of cut on each run means fewer runs.

RIDING MOWERS. Both reel and rotary mowers come in models on which you can ride. These are easy to use, but the lawn should be large enough to warrant the extra cost of the machine. Riding mowers are usually in the $300 price range.

ELECTRIC MOWERS. Some 98 per cent of all power mowers have gasoline engines. But in the city and in built-up areas, where lawns are smaller, electric mowers may be preferred. They are quiet and need little or no maintenance. But you must be careful not to cut the electric cord and always make sure the grass is dry.

SHARPENING THE BLADES. Reel mowers are best sharpened and adjusted by a mower service man at least once a year. Have it done during the winter months so you will have the machine back in spring.

Rotary mowers also must be sharpened regularly. A hand file does a good job. If the blade needs grinding to take out nicks, have it done by a service man so that he can also balance the blade. A blade out of balance will ruin the engine. Always disconnect the spark plug wire while sharpening a rotary. A spin of the blade will set the engine going just as easily as a pull on the starter rope.

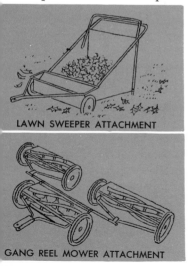

LAWN SWEEPER ATTACHMENT

GANG REEL MOWER ATTACHMENT

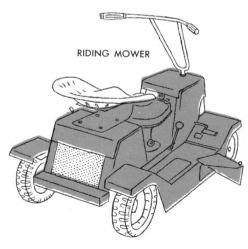

RIDING MOWER

Facts About Garden Tractors. Since the end of World War II, the small garden tractor has come of age. Today there is a tractor for almost every garden—from the postage-stamp urban plot to the large weekend farm. You can pay from $150 to $700 for a garden tractor, depending on its size and the attachments you buy for it.

WHICH TRACTOR FOR YOU? There are four types of garden tractors. Here are facts about each to help you choose which type is best for your needs.

TILLER-TYPE TRACTORS are at the top of the popularity list. These tractors have rotating tines, or blades, that chop into the soil and pulverize it into a fine seedbed. You can use a tiller tractor for cultivating, too, by setting the blades so they cut to a shallower depth.

The tilling mechanism is in front on smaller models. It propels the machine by the action of the cutting tines. Larger machines, which have the tilling mechanism on the rear, are propelled by wheels. Mowing attachments are available for most tractors. For larger machines, additional tools can be bought.

TWO-WHEEL TRACTORS can be equipped to pull traditional farm implements such as a plow, harrow, mowers, and cultivators. Some can also provide power for such chores as sawing wood, rotary mowing, and post-hole digging.

FOUR-WHEEL GARDEN TRACTORS are popular for the large garden or small estate—especially where there is a large lawn to mow. They are generally equipped with a larger and more powerful engine for extra-heavy work. For the weekend farmer, a bonafide farm tractor such as a Ford would be best for continued heavy use.

POWER-PACKAGE TRACTORS are for gardeners who want—or need—more than one power tool. Such a tractor consists of a single engine that easily attaches to various working components. These are not attachments in the true sense. The engine and component work—and look—like a single machine. Components are available for tilling, mowing (reel or rotary), snow blowing, edging and trimming, and for generating electricity and pumping water.

Buying a power-package tractor is an economical way of getting different equipment, since you pay for just one engine. But the disadvantage of the single engine is that only one piece of equipment can be operated at a time.

DON'T EXPECT MIRACLES A small garden tractor will save you time and energy, but there's a limit to what it can do. A tractor with a small 3-H.P. engine will plow, but not as effectively as a farm tractor. The same is true of a tiller. With small tillers, count on going over the ground twice for the best job—the second time, at right angles to the first pass.

When using dozer blades on a garden tractor, you have to make many passes, pushing a small load on each pass. Don't expect bulldozer performance.

A garden tractor isn't as easy to handle as a vacuum cleaner, either. Rocks and heavy clods of soil will push it to one side. But again, keeping a tractor on course is easier and quicker than spading by hand. Take it from tens of thousands of buyers—a tractor eliminates much back-breaking work.

HOW ABOUT A USED TRACTOR? Buying a secondhand tractor can be a saving—or a headache. Best bet is to buy a reconditioned tractor from a factory-authorized dealer. Such a tractor is often as good as a new one. Take a long, critical look at any other used tractor. As a tractor ages, it loses some of its pep and can be balky in starting. Try before you buy.

RENT OR BUY? In some areas you can rent a garden tractor by the day. Sometimes this is best, especially if you have a small place and only do heavy tilling once or twice a year. Also, instead of overloading a small tiller with a job it cannot do—risking damage to the machine— it would be better to rent a machine for the heavy work and use the small tractor for cultivating and mowing.

POWER-PACKAGE ENGINE ATTACHES TO CULTIVATOR MOWER, OTHER IMPLEMENTS.

Improving Your Soil

Few soils are ideal for growing plants. A soil may lack plant nutrients, have a poor consistency, be too acid, etc. But fortunately soils can easily be improved.

WHY FERTILIZE? Nitrogen, phosphorus, and potash are the plant foods most commonly needed by the soil of your garden or lawn. And they are the three main elements in commercial fertilizers.

The amounts of these elements in the fertilizer are listed in a formula. That's the 10-10-10, 5-10-5, or other number combination you see on the fertilizer bag or its tag.

These numbers express the percentage of each element in the fertilizer. The first figure always stands for nitrogen, the second for a phosphorus compound, and the third for potash. For example, a 5-10-5 fertilizer contains 5 per cent nitrogen, 10 per cent phosphate, and 5 per cent potash. The other 80 per cent may include some minor elements, but is mostly a carrier. Usually the fertilizer that delivers a pound of the basic elements for the least cost is the best buy.

What do these elements do for your plants?

NITROGEN is the element that brings fast vegetative growth. It can turn lawns miraculously green almost overnight. Nitrogen can be supplied by an organic source, such as manure, or by inorganic fertilizers.

PHOSPHORUS is needed for root growth and fruit or flower production. It stimulates seedlings and helps young plants get off to a fast, vigorous start. Manures contain some phosphorus, but the best sources are a mixed fertilizer with a high phosphorus ratio, a super-phosphate, or a treble super-phosphate.

POTASH increases plant vigor and resistance to disease. Mixed fertilizers usually have enough of this element.

VALUE OF COMPOST AND PEAT   A compost made of leaves, lawn clippings, and rotted vegetation from the garden works wonders. It binds a sandy soil so that the soil holds more water and nutrients. It makes a clay soil more porous and easier to work. It teems with billions of microorganisms that aid plant growth.

Build your compost pile in layers about a foot deep. Sprinkle a cup of fertilizer per 10 square feet over each layer, and cover with ½ inch of soil. Let the pile rot through one summer before using it.

Peat moss improves soil in the same ways as compost. It's also useful around shrubs and small trees. Peat bales should be well broken up and soaked with water before spreading over soil to a depth of 1 to 2 inches.

How to Measure Fertilizer

Throughout this book you can find many recommendations on how much fertilizer to apply to this plant or that. You may also get recommendations from your county agricultural agent after having your soil tested. The table below will help you translate the recommended amounts into figures that suit the size of your garden.

Simply find the recommended amount in the table and read across to the amount that will satisfy your need. For example, if the recommendation is 7 pounds per 1,000 square feet, you can use 1½ cups per 100 square feet, ½ cup per 10 feet of a row spaced 3 feet from other rows, etc. In general, 1 pound of fertilizer is equal to 2 cups.

Weights per 1,000 sq. ft.	Volume Measures for 100 sq. ft.	Rates per 10 ft. for Rows Spaced—		Rates per Plant, for Plants Spaced—	
		3 ft.	2 ft.	5 x 5 ft.	2¼ x 2¼ ft.
pounds	pints	cups	cups	cups	cups
45	5	3	2	2½	7½
38	4	2½	1½	2	6½
28	3	1¾	1¼	1½	5
23	2½	1½	1	1¼	4
18	2	1¼	¾	1	3¼
14	1½	¾	½	¾	2½
			tbs.		
9	1	½	6	½	1½
	cups			*tbs.*	
7	1½	½	5	6	1
		tbs.			*tsps.*
4¾	1	5	3¼	4	2½
2¼	½	2½	1½	2	1¼
ounces	*tbs.*		*tsps.*		
18	4	1¼	2½	1	½
		tsps.			
5	1	1	½	¼	⅙

Lime Unlocks the Soil. Lime corrects acidity in your soil, sweetening it to the level where most flowers and vegetables do best. Lime liberates soil phosphate, making more available to plants. It aids growth of helpful soil organisms and stimulates healthier plant growth.

Most flowers and vegetables do well in soil ranging from slightly acid to neutral. Sulfur can increase acidity where you want to grow an acid-loving plant such as an azalea or rhododendron.

Before applying lime, the soil's acidity should be checked. Too much lime will lock up soluble forms of elements such as phosphorus, iron, zinc, and manganese.

Testing Your Soil. To find out what your soil needs in the way of fertilizer or lime, you can test the soil yourself with a home-test kit (available from Sudbury Laboratories, Sudbury, Mass.). You simply mix a soil sample with certain chemicals, and the resulting solution

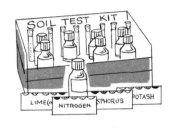

tion takes on a distinctive color. Comparing this with a color chart tells you whether the soil is low on one of the major plant food elements and, if so, how much of it to add. You can also check the soil's acidity.

If you prefer, you can send soil samples to a soil-testing laboratory. Your county agricultural agent can suggest one.

Here is how to collect soil samples:

1. Take a small amount of soil from several places in the garden down to a depth of 5 or 6 inches.

2. Mix well and send cupful of air-dry sample to the laboratory. Include a note telling what you plan to grow.

Apply fertilizer and lime in the amounts recommended by the soil testers.

USE COFFEE GROUNDS

Spread your old coffee grounds around acid-loving plants. The grounds will reduce the pH content of the soil and make such plants as these really thrive: rhododendron, azalea, clethra, heather, blueberry, sourwood, mountain laurel, trailing arbutus, holly, and lady slipper orchids. Keep grounds away from lilac bushes.

Mulches Save Work and Water. A good coating of mulch in a garden or around the ornamentals is the mark of the experienced gardener. Mulching cuts down on weed growth and, consequently, on hoeing. It prevents evaporation of water, which makes rainfall go farther. Soil is cooler under the mulch—perhaps 20 degrees or more—and that aids growth, too.

There are a great many mulches available. Some of the more popular ones are listed in the chart on pages 138-139. Choose a mulch for your garden that is cheap and readily available. And you'll be happier with it in the long run if it is attractive.

Mulching eliminates root injury that often accompanies hoeing or cultivating. Legume hays and grass, used as mulches, add nutrients to the soil. Mulched trees in orchards consistently outyield cultivated trees.

Organisms that cause organic matter in mulches to decompose use nitrogen. That's why it's a good idea to apply extra nitrogen before mulching. When plants tend to have light green or yellowish leaves, apply ½ pound of ammonium nitrate per 100 square feet.

Recently, two man-made mulches, aluminum foil and plastic, have been used with much success.

Aluminum foil mulch has increased yields two to five times and has eliminated weeding, watering, and cultivating problems. For example, Pennsylvania State University researchers rolled heavy-duty foil on the ground and weighted it down with loose earth or stones. They made crisscross cuts in the foil to put in transplants. The foil then was folded back around the plants. As a result, cucumber yields were increased as much as five times. Tomato yields were nearly tripled. Peppers, head lettuce, and Lima beans prospered, too.

During the day, aluminum reflects heat. At night, it holds back heat that otherwise would be radiated away.

Black plastic polyethylene is gaining wide popularity as a garden mulch. It clings to the ground better than foil and will last 3 or 4 years. Practically no weeds come through—and that ends hoeing.

Before laying plastic on a row, dig a shallow trench along the center of the row. An occasional hole in the plastic, along the bottom of this trench, permits rainfall to drain through.

Wind does not bother plastic if its edges are covered with soil and if a bit of soil is placed on the plastic every 3 to 4 feet. Cost of this material is about a half cent per 100 square feet. Large-scale operators have found that work savings soon pay for the plastic.

YOUR GUIDE TO GARDEN MULCHES

Material	Where to Get It	Best Uses, Comments
Aluminum foil	Garden supply, department, or grocery stores	Handy in starting vegetables. Can be used a second year. Too bright to use for ornamental plantings.
Asphalt	Paving contractors	Light application holds soil on steep banks until grass cover starts.
Buckwheat hulls	Garden supply stores	Fine texture, long life, and good color make this a good ornamental mulching material.
Cocoa-bean hulls	Chocolate companies	Clean, good color.
Cornstalks	Farms or gardens	Very coarse, but useful in holding down other mulches. Attracts pests.
Ground corncobs	Farms or local grain elevators	Good mulch, but not attractive for ornamental beds.
Hay	Farms, acreages, or feed stores	Widely used mulch. Legumes such as alfalfa or clover decay rapidly and supply considerable nitrogen.
Lawn clippings	From any lawn	Satisfactory mulch if you let grass dry first. Green clippings tend to heat soil and to mat down.
Leafmold	From compost pile or woods	This makes a mulch particularly well suited for wildflower
Leaves	From lawn or woods	Make better mulch if composted. Maple and poplar tend to mat. Oak good for rhododendrons.

Material	Where to Get It	Best Uses, Comments
Peanut hulls	Peanut mills	Good cheap mulch in South. Not very attractive for ornamentals.
Peat moss	Garden supply stores	Has a fine texture and good color. It does have a tendency to dry out and then become impervious to water.
Pine needles	Wherever conifers grow	Attractive and useful for wildflower and other plantings.
Plastic film	Garden supply stores	Practical for large garden areas. Has slits to let water get into soil. Kills weeds and saves moisture. Easy to cover with ¼' soil if desirable.
Sawdust	Sawmills or lumberyards	Good general mulch. Sometimes causes nitrogen shortage, which can be corrected with fertilizer.
Straw	Farms or feedstores	Makes a coarse mulch that is more durable than hay. Cheap, easily available mulch.
Strawy manure	Farms or stables	Provides some nutrients. May burn plants if applied when fresh.
Wood chips	Utilities using wood chippers	Coarser mulch than sawdust, but less likely to cause nitrogen deficiency. Makes a good mulch.

—*Based on information from Brooklyn Botanic Garden*

Fruit—For Beauty Plus

Fruit growing can be an interesting hobby, whether you have a single tree, a few berry plants, or a whole orchard. Many fruit trees will add a touch of beauty to your yard, with a display of blossoms in the spring and colorful fruit later in the year. And fruit is never tastier than when freshly picked. Watching the fruit develop can in itself be a fascinating experience.

If your yard is small, consider dwarf fruit trees. Since they take up less space, you can plant a larger variety of fruits. Ask your local nurseryman what grows best in your area.

For More and Better Fruit. Fruit trees generally begin to bear fruit from two to seven years after you plant them, depending on the type of tree. Here are suggestions on caring for fruit trees.

HOW TO PLANT
A FRUIT TREE

SET TREE AT SAME DEPTH AS PREVIOUSLY PLANTED, USING STICK AS GUIDE.

ADD TOPSOIL, PEAT MOSS, WATER LIBERALLY.

FILL REST OF HOLE. ADD MULCH. USE FOIL WRAPPER AS GUARD AGAINST PESTS.

MULCHING   Fruit yields are increased by mulching. It conserves moisture in the soil and discourages weed growth. Apply a layer of about 6 inches of wheat, straw, hay, or other mulching material around the tree. The material will soon settle to less than half its original thickness, forming a mat. The mulched area should extend just beyond the spread of the branches. Each year add material to replace what has rotted and extend the area as much as the plant has grown.

One of the disadvantages of mulching is that it makes a good nesting place for mice, and mice damage young fruit trees. The most practical way to guard against mice is to put ¼-inch mesh hardware cloth around the tree. (Or use Rabbit-Wrap, an aluminum foil designed for such problems.) The circular guard should be about 6 inches in diameter and should extend from several inches below the surface of the soil to the first branches.

FERTILIZING   For each year the tree is old, apply ¼ pound of ammonium sulfate for apples and plums; ⅓ pound for cherries and peaches. For example, an 8-year-old apple tree would require 2 pounds. Or, instead of ammonium sulfate, use half as much ammonium nitrate or twice as much mixed fertilizer containing 10 per cent nitrogen. The shoot growth of trees should be 8 to 15 inches a year. If your trees grow less, use a fertilizer with a higher percentage of nitrogen; if they grow more, reduce nitrogen.

SPRAYING   A combination fruit spray for both insects and disease is recommended. Spray 4 times to get top quality fruit and berries. Check the manufacturer's directions for times to spray, since they vary.

WATERING   Newly planted trees should receive 5 to 10 gallons of water weekly when there is no rain. The bigger they get, the more water they need.

Fruit Pruning Tips

YOUNG FRUIT TREES   Prune your trees in late winter or early spring. A 1-year-old unbranched tree should be cut back to 12 to 18 inches high so it will form low lateral branches. Branches of a 2-year-old tree should be pruned until there are two well-spaced lateral branches and a leader to form the framework of the tree (see drawing).

BEARING TREES   Head back branches that are getting out of hand. Remove small, weak inside branches. Keep the tree open so there are no dense shaded areas.

DWARF TREES   These are pruned in the same way as larger trees, but the amount of pruning is less. Dwarf trees should be headed lower.

GRAPES   Grape vines need bold pruning. They should be cut back to a few buds to get them to bear. Here's how: After planting, cut back to 2 buds. Use the most vigorous vine as a single trunk. Tie it to 2 horizontal wires to establish a training system with 4 vines, as shown. Each year prune back, leaving 40 to 50 buds. You'll have to cut away as much as 2 pounds of vine per plant.

RASPBERRIES   Remove 2-year-old fruiting canes as soon as harvest is complete. Cut them off close to the ground so they have no chance to spread disease to new shoots.

Black raspberries and blackberries respond to summer pinching. Pinch off ends of new shoots when they reach 18 to 24 inches. The next spring, shorten the lateral branches that result from this pinching.

Red raspberries should not be pinched because this makes them more likely to be killed during winter. Before growth starts in spring, cut unbranched canes back to about 3 to 4 feet. Remove weak canes.

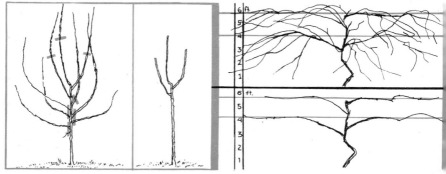

TWO-YEAR-OLD TREE BEFORE, AFTER PRUNING   GRAPE VINE BEFORE AND AFTER PRUNING

Fruit Planting Guide

	Feet Between Rows	Feet Between Plants	When to Expect Fruit	Yield per Mature Plant
Tree Fruits				
Apple (dwarf)	10-15	10-15	2-3 yrs.	6-10 bu.
Pear (dwarf)	10-15	10-15	2-3 yrs.	2-4 bu.
Peach (dwarf)	10-15	10-15	2-3 yrs.	1-2 bu.
Cherry (sweet)	20	20	4-7 yrs.	7-8 bu.
Cherry (tart)	20	20	3 yrs.	3-4 bu.
Plum	20	20	3-4 yrs.	3-5 bu.
Small Fruits				
Grapes	10	10	2 yrs.	8-10 lb.
Raspberries	8	6	1 yr.	2 qt.
Blackberries	8	3	1 yr.	2 qt.
Currants	8	3	1 yr.	3 qt.
Blueberries	6	4	1 yr.	2 qt.
Strawberries	3	2	1 yr.	1 pt.+

Building a Tile Storage Bin

A drain tile that is 2 feet in diameter and 2 feet long, or larger, can be made into a storage bin for fruits and vegetables that need to be kept moist and cool. Here's how:

1. Dig a hole 6 inches deeper than the tile and just large enough so it fits snugly.

2. Place three 8-inch-long bricks on end at the bottom of the hole with flat sides to the wall. These form a base for the tile, leaving 8 inches of exposed soil. The lip of the tile is 2 inches above ground.

3. Put a few shovelfuls of crushed rock or coarse gravel in the bottom. Mound soil up to the tile's lip around the sides.

4. Lay a 36 x 36 inch piece of ½-inch mesh hardware cloth over the top. Cover with about 4 inches of dry leaves for insulation.

5. Put on a waterproof cover—an old large tub will do the trick.

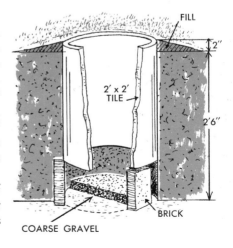

FILL

2'

2' x 2' TILE

2'6"

BRICK

COARSE GRAVEL

Strawberries—the Most Popular Garden Fruit. Here's a fruit anyone can grow. About 100 plants will produce enough strawberries for an average family.

PLANTING Buy new virus-free plants in early spring. Before planting, work into the soil 1 to 1½ pounds of 10-10-10 fertilizer per 100 square feet. Prune dry leaves from the crown of each plant, leaving only 2 or 3 well-developed leaves. Remove all roots longer than 4 inches. Set plants 24 inches apart in rows 42 inches apart.

Use a liquid or other "plant starter" type fertilizer after planting. Keep the plants watered. On light soil, they need 1 inch of water every 10 days. There seldom is that much rain.

CARE Here are six steps for growing better berries:

1. Control weeds. Start cultivating a few days after plants are set. Or mulch the bed 2 weeks after setting, but no deeper than 2 inches.

2. Pinch out blossom clusters the first year (on everbearing plants, until mid-July). This makes for a stronger plant.

3. Side-dress with a high-nitrogen fertilizer when plants begin to form runners and again in early August. Each time, use 2 pounds per 100 feet of row or 1 teaspoonful per plant.

4. In northern states cover berries with marsh hay or coarse straw for winter protection. Apply when ground has frozen ½-inch deep or when temperature drops to 20 degrees. Remove as soon as spring growth starts.

5. Apply an all-purpose spray just before bloom and again 10 days later.

6. Renew the bed after harvest. Cultivate out everything except the center 6 or 8 inches of the row. Hoe and thin the remaining 6 or 8 inches. Feed with 8 pounds of 10-10-10 fertilizer per 100 feet of row.

HOW TO PLANT A STRAWBERRY PLANT

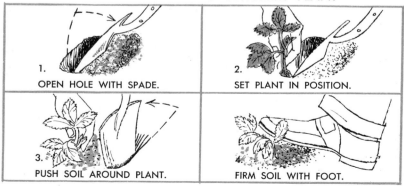

1. OPEN HOLE WITH SPADE.

2. SET PLANT IN POSITION.

3. PUSH SOIL AROUND PLANT.

4. FIRM SOIL WITH FOOT.

These beautiful spring-flowering trees will later yield delicious fruit—they're apricots! What's more, they will provide summer-long shade, but remain small enough not to rob neighboring plants of sunlight. Below: *Colorful blossoms of two other popular fruit trees—apple* (left) *and Japanese cherry.*

Spring, summer, and fall flowers *from perennials and bulbs provide a pageant of color and fragrance, year after year.* Top photographs, left to right: *day lilies and funkia; tulips and forget-me-nots; gold band lilies; Oriental poppies.* Right: *masses of autumn-blooming chrysanthemums.* Below: *Selma Lagerlof daffodils.*

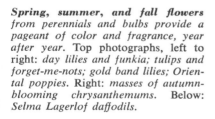

Flowering annuals *provide profuse bloom quickly, at low cost.* Above: *Lavender petunias combine with the last spring-flowering bulbs to form riot of color.*

Big and bright, *zinnias* (left) *are among the most useful annuals for home gardens.* Below: *Mixture of annuals includes marigolds, petunias, zinnias, and scarlet salvia.*

Bedding begonias, *petunias, scented geraniums* (above) *spill out of urns on steps.* Right: *Dooryard garden filled with annuals.* Below: *Nasturtiums bloom in front of the fence, mixed annuals behind it.*

Varieties of three indoor favorites are (above, left to right) *Olympic geranium, Emperor Frederick gloxinia, Christmas begonia.* Below, left: *Grape-ivy, philo-dendron, and peperomia provide permanent greenery for entranceway planter. Daffodils, tulips, hyacinths, and a geranium give cheerful springtime welcome.* Below, right: *Variegated-leaved Pothos is an easily grown house plant.*

Plants grow at ground level *in this sunroom* (above). *They include gardenias, eucharis, jacarandas, Chinese evergreen, and bromeliads. Caladiums provide foliage color outdoors. Left: Geraniums come in a bewildering array of colors and leaf shapes. Sunlight makes them bloom. They grow well both in winter window gardens and in outdoor plant boxes.*

151

Vines can do wonders! *Opposite page: Lavender wisteria is glorious in May, provides terrace with a leafy bower and cool shade in summer and fall. Orange berries of espaliered pyracantha last all winter, are attractive against white wall. Paul's Scarlet rose makes garage front special. This page: Heavenly Blue morning glories give cooling color all summer, as they perch on fences or trellises. Everblooming climbing red roses decorate wooden fence. Hardy ivy trained up and across porch posts gives special appeal to ranch-style house.*

Rock formations and flowers *can be combined to glorify sweeping slopes, to edge winding paths and steps, to fill small nooks and corners with charm.* Left: *Informal bayside rock garden in June.* Below, far left: *Double pink petunias and blue-leaved sempervivums.* Below, left: *Sun filters through tall trees to highlight rockery in natural woodland setting.* Above: *Masses of golden alyssum and creeping rambler roses in rocky coastal setting.* Below: *Rockery bank along sidewalk is ablaze with purple, lavender, and gold in May.*

For pure enjoyment, *a greenhouse attached to the house has many advantages over a self-standing one. Greatest of these is accessibility, especially when the rain pours or the snow flies. Style of greenhouse above compliments that of house. Brick walk, separated from flower border by slow-growing, tidy boxwood, leads visitors straight to the wonders to be discovered in any greenhouse.*

Orchid   *Tuberous begonia*   *African violet*

These two small greenhouses burst with the flowers of plants easily grown in a cool, sunny, moist atmosphere. Flowering plants visible include hyacinths, daffodils, azaleas, cinerarias, begonias, carnations, snapdragons, geraniums, pansies, sweet alyssum, freesias, petunias, cyclamen, ranunculus, and Easter lilies. Many of these flowers give a bonus of fragrance.

Outdoor living area (above) *is brightened by border of lavender-blue ageratum and chrysanthemums in fall hues.* Below: *Potted oleanders and geraniums dress up stone terrace and steps; climbing gym appeals to young acrobats.*

Lighting gardens and pools at night not only extends the hours they can be lived in and enjoyed, but also creates effects of unusual, even ethereal, beauty. Use lights as an artist uses colors on his palette. Right: *Night lighting dramatizes specimen pine, which is reflected in pool. Tree's foliage is illuminated by two 75-watt bulbs in fixtures with green lenses; trunk by one 30-watt lamp.* Below: *Colored lights give California garden exotic effect—two 40-watt lamps with green lenses enrich elephant ears in foreground, while 60-watt amber light accentuates papyrus against the sky.*

Climbing roses have many uses. Above, left: *Paul's Scarlet rose combines colorfully with geraniums in hanging pots and dwarf marigolds in brick planter to provide striking entranceway display.* Above: *Climbing roses are crowning glory to full-scale rose garden.* Below: *Roses transform fence into handsome landscaping detail.* Left: *For beauty of form and color, the rose is hard to beat.*

Your Vegetable Garden

Vegetables from your own garden taste better and *are* better than anything you can buy in a store. There's nothing to compare with tomatoes ripened on the vine and lettuce that has hardly had a minute to wilt. You can enjoy your own vegetables in the winter, too, by picking and freezing them at the right stage of ripeness.

There are other dividends. Research shows your family gets more vitamins from garden-fresh produce. For example, just six hours after it is picked, sweet corn loses much of its vitamin A. Vegetable gardening is a boon to the budget, too. The average urban gardener who has a small vegetable garden can save at least $100 on his grocery bill, estimates Robert F. Stevens, University of Delaware horticulturist. Vegetable gardening, of course, takes work, but don't underestimate the satisfaction you'll get from just working the soil.

Before You Plant. Plan your garden on paper. Here are guides to help you make the most of your space and prevent the extra work of overproduction:

1. Locate perennials such as asparagus and rhubarb at one side of the garden.

2. Plant corn and other tall plants where they won't shade smaller ones.

3. Plant fast-growing, quick-maturing crops together to make it easier to replant to new crops.

4. Select crops you know the family likes. Don't overplant new varieties—try them first.

5. Make sure your row spacing is wide enough for your cultivator.

6. Run rows north and south, when possible, to avoid shading.

Small Vegetable Garden. Here is a planting table for a garden 25 by 30 feet. Crops in parentheses can be planted in indicated rows after early crops are harvested.

Planting	Row No.	Width	Vegetable
	1	12″	Early peas (snap beans late)
	2	12″	Second early peas (lettuce & kohlrabi late)
	3	12″	Spinach (spinach late)
April 15	4	12″	Leaf lettuce (spinach late)
	5	12″	Onion sets (radish late)
	6	12″	Onion seed planted with radish (turnips late)
	7	24″	Early cabbage plants
	8	24″	Carrots planted with radish
May 1	9	18″	N. Z. Spinach. Beets planted with radish
	10	30″	Tomato seed
	11	24″	Snap beans
May 15	12	24″	Tomato plants
	13	24″	Snap beans
May 20	14	18″	Lima beans
	15	24″	Summer squash or peppers. Cucumbers or eggplant
		18″	(Border strip)

—Table from University of Illinois

DEPTH OF PLANTING DEPENDS ON SEED SIZE

SMALL SEED ¼"-½" MEDIUM SEED ½"-1" LARGE SEED 1"-1½"

BANDING WITH FERTILIZER

FERTILIZER IN FURROW

Planting Pointers. Work the seedbed just before planting. Otherwise weeds may come up before the plants. Plant in straight rows. This makes cultivating easier, and you're less likely to prune roots.

The smaller the seed, the shallower it should be planted. Also, plant all seeds shallower in early spring and in heavy soil. Cover seed with fine moist soil, and firm the soil by tamping lightly with the back of a hoe.

Plants make best use of a small amount of fertilizer if it is placed in bands. Make two furrows about 3 inches on either side of the row and slightly deeper than 3 inches. Apply 2 pounds of 5-10-10 fertilizer per 100 feet of row, 1 pound on each side.

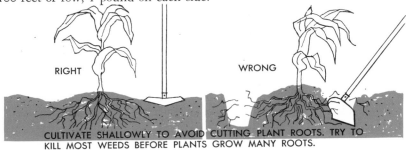

RIGHT WRONG

CULTIVATE SHALLOWLY TO AVOID CUTTING PLANT ROOTS. TRY TO KILL MOST WEEDS BEFORE PLANTS GROW MANY ROOTS.

A Tom Thumb Garden. Want a vegetable garden, but have little space? Plant these midgets:

MIDGET SWEET CORN grows on 30-inch-high plants. It has 4-inch ears and matures in 60 days.

MIDGET MUSKMELON, developed at University of Minnesota, is only 4 inches across. It has 3-foot vines.

TINY TIM TOMATO is grown on a dwarf plant that will even fit a flower pot inside the home.

NEW HAMPSHIRE WATERMELON is 7 inches long, fits easily in refrigerator. It can be planted very early and grows well in northern states.

DWARF CUCUMBER, 4 inches long, grows on compact vines 18 to 24 inches long.

You can get a package containing all of these seeds for $1 from Farmer Seed and Nursery Co., Faribault, Minn.

YOUR VEGETABLE PLANTING GUIDE

Vegetable	To Seed 100 Feet*	Width of Rows** (inches)	Space Between Plants in Row (inches)	Depth of Planting of Seeds (inches)	Time to Maturity (days)
Beans, dwarf snap	1 lb.	18-24	3-4	½-1	50-65
Beans, pole snap	½ lb.	36	24	½-1	50-75
Beans, green shell	1 lb.	24	2-4	½-1	90-100
Beans, dry shell	1 lb.	24	2-4	½-1	90-100
Beans, dwarf Lima	1 lb.	24-30	4-6	½-1	75-80
Beans, pole Lima	¾ lb.	30-36	24	½-1	80-100
Beets	1 oz.	12-18	2-4	¼-½	50-70
Broccoli	¼ oz.	18-24	18-24	¼-½	75-100
Brussels sprouts	¼ oz.	18-24	18-24	¼-½	90-130
Cabbage, early	¼ oz.	18-24	15-18	(plants)	60-90
Cabbage, late	¼ oz.	18-24	18-24	½	90-120
Cabbage, Chinese	½ oz.	18-24	8-10	½	75-100
Carrots	½ oz.	12-18	2-3	¼-½	55-90
Cauliflower, early	¼ oz.	30-36	18-24	½	75-100
Cauliflower, late	¼ oz.	30-36	18-24	½	90-120
Celery, early	¼ oz.	18-36	6	(plants)	75-100
Celery, late	¼ oz.	18-36	6	⅛	100-120
Celeriac	¼ oz.	18-24	6	⅛	90-115
Chicory	½ oz.	18	3-6	¼-½	120-130
Chives		12-18	8-12	(plants)	
Corn, sweet (early)	¼ lb.	24-36	8-10	1½	70-80
Corn, sweet (late)	¼ lb.	32-36	10-12	1½	85-100
Cress (upland)	¼ oz.	12-18	3-4	¼-½	60-80
Cucumber	½ oz.	48-60	12-48	1-1½	60-80
Dandelion	½ oz.	18	8	¼-½	175-200
Eggplant	¼ oz.	24	18-24	(plants)	90-100
Endive	½ oz.	12-18	8-12	¼-½	60-90
Horseradish		24	12	6	180
Kale	½ oz.	18-24	8-12	½	50-200
Kohlrabi	¼ oz.	18-24	2-4	½	60-75
Leek	½ oz.	12-18	2-4	½	130-180
Lettuce	¼ oz.	12-18	8-12	¼-½	45-75

YOUR VEGETABLE PLANTING GUIDE

Vegetable	To Seed 100 Feet*	Width of Rows** (inches)	Space Between Plants in Row (inches)	Depth of Planting of Seeds (inches)	Time to Maturity (days)
Muskmelon	½ oz.	48-60	12-48	½-1	85-100
Onion, plants	½ oz.	12-18	2-3	(plants)	110
Onion, sets	2 lb.	12-18	3-4	½	100-120
Onion, seed	½ oz.	12-18	4-5	¼-½	130-180
Onion (for sets)	2 oz.	12-15	crowded	¼-½	90-100
Parsley	½ oz.	12-18	6	¼-½	60-90
Parsnip	½ oz.	18-24	3-4	¼-½	95-110
Peas	1 lb.	18-24	2	1-1½	50-80
Pepper	¼ oz.	18-24	12-18	(plants)	70-90
Potato, sweet	1 pk.	30	12-18	(plants)	115-125
Pumpkin (vine)	½ oz.	72-96	72-96	1	90-110
Radish	1 oz.	12-18	1-2	½	25-35
Rhubarb	½ oz.	30	2-3	(plants)	(2 yrs.)
Rutabaga	½ oz.	18-24	4-6	½	90-120
Salsify	1 oz.	12-18	2-3	½	140-150
Spinach	1 oz.	12-18	3-6	½	40-60
Spinach, New Zealand	1 oz.	24-36	18-24	1	60-80
Squash, winter	½ oz.	72-96	72-96	1	90-110
Squash, summer	1 oz.	36-48	36-48	1	50-80
Swiss chard	1 oz.	18-24	6-8	½-1	50-60
Tomato	⅛ oz.	36-48	36-48	(plants)	75-100
Tomato, staked	⅛ oz.	24-30	15-18	(plants)	75-100
Turnip	½ oz.	12-18	3-4	¼-½	50-80
Turnip for greens	1 oz.	5	12-18	¼-½	45-50
Watermelon	½ oz.	72-120	72-96	1	70-95

*For shorter or longer rows, vary the amount proportionately.
**Distance between rows may vary with type of cultivator you use.

Tips on Growing Tomatoes

SETTING PLANTS   After there is no more danger of frost, set plants about 2 to 3 inches deeper than they were in the flat or pot in which you bought them or grew them from seed. If you plan to stake and prune, set plants 16 to 20 inches apart in rows 2 to 3 feet apart. If not, allow 12 to 16 square feet per plant. (Leggy plants should be set in a trench so that 5 to 6 inches of their tops are above the ground.)

FERTILIZING   Tomatoes are heavy feeders, so be liberal with fertilizer. A good general ratio is 35 pounds of 5-10-10 per 1,000 square feet.

CULTIVATING   Tomato feeder roots are near the surface. So after plants are established, cultivate less than 2 inches deep. Kill weeds when plants are small.

STAKING AND PRUNING   This pays off when space is limited. Yield per plant is lower, but you can have more plants. Use a 1-inch stake 5 feet tall for each plant. Limit plant growth to a single stalk. Pinch out side branches. Use strips of cloth to tie the plant to the stake.

MULCHING   This helps control weeds, conserves moisture, and keeps soil cooler. Mulch just before fruit setting begins with 4 to 6 inches of material. Too early mulching checks vine growth.

BLIGHT CONTROL   Blight and other diseases can be controlled by spraying or dusting with a fungicide-insecticide, by using disease-free plants, by setting plants in the open where the sun can dry their foliage, and by planting as far from potatoes as possible.

Add Fun and Flavor with Herbs.   Variety is the key to a good herb garden. A few plants of each kind are enough to add spice to the family cooking. Here are suggestions for growing herbs:

CHIVES: Set bulblet clumps 8 inches apart after the ground thaws in spring. Keep plants clipped. These fast-growing plants make a good border. Grow them all winter on your window sill.

DILL: Sow seed after the last spring frost. Do not thin plants. Dill is an annual, but may reseed itself.

MINT: Set out plant divisions in the spring. Choose a moist soil. This plant spreads rapidly.

Plant a Permanent Garden. Perennial vegetables such as asparagus and rhubarb should be planted at one side of the garden where they won't be disturbed during spring plowing.

HOW TO GROW ASPARAGUS Buy 1-year-old plants (or raise your own from seed). Set them in furrows 6 to 8 inches deep, with roots spread. Cover with 2 to 3 inches of soil. Gradually fill the furrows as the plants grow. Furrows should be filled at the end of the first season.

ASPARAGUS
SET IN FURROW

Asparagus responds well to fertilizer. Use one with a 5-10-10 ratio. Apply 1 pound per 100 square feet before planting and 1½ pounds per 100 square feet on mature beds before and after cutting.

HOW TO GROW RHUBARB A few of these plants, which hail from Siberia, will keep your family in delicious sauce and pie. Plant rhubarb roots in the early spring. To increase growth, apply manure or 1½ pounds of 10-10-10 fertilizer per plant each year. The plants will produce their first crop the next summer. To harvest the crop, pull stalks; do not cut. Remove seed flower stalks, since they use up food reserves and slow stalk growth. About every 7 years dig up roots, divide, and replant.

TO HARVEST RHUBARB,
YANK STALK TO ONE SIDE.

GARDEN SAGE: Set plants 12 inches apart when the ground is workable. Next spring, cut back new growth to 6 inches. Divide plants with woody growth at the roots each spring.

GARDEN THYME: When the ground has warmed, set plants 8 inches apart. Every 3 years, divide plants to keep them from getting woody.

HORSERADISH: Early in spring, plant root cuttings 1 foot apart in rows 3 feet apart. Plant them so they slant slightly. Root tops should be 3 inches below ground. Apply well-rotted manure, if possible.

MINT

SAGE

THYME

Gardener's Directory

Garden Clubs. Joining a garden club can make gardening more fun. Local garden clubs hold regular meetings, have interesting speakers, put on garden shows, engage in civic improvement projects, and, together with state and national groups, take an active interest in conservation. Some sponsor junior garden clubs.

Local garden clubs are generally affiliated with one of the three national organizations described below. Write them for information on garden clubs in your area or how to start one.

National Council of State Garden Clubs, Inc., 4401 Magnolia Ave., St. Louis 10, Mo. This organization is made up of 46 state garden club councils, comprising 12,870 local clubs, and has more than 400,000 members. Publication: *The National Gardener,* $1 a year.

The Garden Club of America, 598 Madison Ave., New York, N.Y., is an organization of 166 local garden clubs, with a total of 11,000 members. Publication: *The Garden Club of America Bulletin,* $3 a year.

Men's Garden Clubs of America: George A. Spader, Executive Secretary, Morrisville, N.Y. This is a national organization of about 200 local men's garden clubs. Membership: about 10,000.

Garden Specialty Societies. If you're a fan of a particular flower or gardening activity, you may want to join a society devoted to it. Here's a list of such societies.

African Violet Society of America: J. Hapgood Brooks III, executive director, P.O. Box 1326, Knoxville, Tenn.

American Amaryllis Society: Dr. Thomas Whitaker, executive secretary, Box 150, La Jolla, Calif.

American Begonia Society: Mrs. Daisy Walker, secretary, 3628 Revere Ave., Los Angeles 39, Calif.

American Camellia Society: Arthur C.

Brown, executive secretary, Box 2398, University Station, Gainesville, Fla.

American Carnation Society: Francis A. Baur, secretary, R.R. 1, Box 562, New Augusta, Ind.

American Daffodil Society: Miss Estelle L. Sharp, secretary, Berwyn, Pa.

American Dahlia Society: Edward B. Lloyd, secretary, 10 Crestmont Rd., Montclair, N.J.

American Delphinium Society: William

Hall, secretary, 38253 Wilson Mills Rd., Willoughby, Ohio.

American Fern Society: Prof. Mildred E. Faust, secretary, Department of Botany, Syracuse University, Syracuse, N.Y.

American Fuchsia Society: C. T. Le-Hew, secretary, 1633 Moreland Dr., Alameda, Calif.

American Gesneria Society: E. E. Hammond, president, 109 Copeland Lane, Irvington, Calif.

American Gloxinia Society: Kenneth W. Fielder, secretary, 4139 S. Rockford Pl., Tulsa, Okla.

American Hibiscus Society: Mrs. C. H. Calais, executive secretary, Goldenrod-Orlando, Fla.

American Horticultural Council: Donald Wyman, secretary, Arnold Arboretum, Jamaica Plain 30, Mass.

American Iris Society: Clifford W. Benson, secretary, 2237 Tower Grove Blvd., St. Louis, Mo.

American Orchid Society: Gordon W. Dillon, executive secretary, Botanical Museum of Harvard University, Cambridge 38, Mass.

American Penstemon Society: Mrs. Edward M. Babb, secretary, 215 Lambert St., Portland, Me.

American Peony Society: George W. Peyton, secretary, Box No. 1, Rapidan, Va.

American Poinsettia Society: Mrs. R. E. Gaunt, executive secretary, Box 94, Mission, Tex.

American Primrose Society: Mrs. Anne Siepman, secretary, 3616 N. E. Belle-vue-Redmond Rd., Kirkland, Wash.

American Rhododendron Society: Mrs. Ruth M. Hansen, secretary, 3514 N. Russet St., Portland 17, Ore.

American Rock Garden Society: Edgar L. Totten, secretary, 238 Sheridan Ave., Hohokus, N. J.

American Rose Society: James P. Gurney, executive secretary, 4048 Roselea Pl., Columbus 14, Ohio.

Bulb Society: Constance Williams, corresponding secretary, 709 North Stoneman Ave., Alhambra, Calif.

Cactus and Succulent Society of America: Mrs. Ethel G. Rush, secretary, 820 West 115 St., Los Angeles 44, Calif.

Dwarf Iris Society: Mrs. Walter Welch, secretary, Middlebury, Ind.

National Tulip Society: Felix R. Tyroler, secretary, 55 West 42 St., New York 36, N.Y.

North American Lily Society: Mrs. W. T. Mears, secretary, Route 3, Box 99, Anderson, Ind.

Plant Propagation Society: Kenneth W. Reisch, secretary, Department of Horticulture, Ohio State University, Columbus 10, Ohio.

Where to Get Garden Catalogues

The biggest and best library in existence for the average gardener consists of garden catalogues. Here is a partial list of concerns that will send you their catalogues. Most are free. A few, in full color, cost from 5c to $1, as noted. Specialties of each concern are listed.

General Nursery Stock

Ackerman Nurseries, Bridgman, Mich. Fruits, ornamental trees, roses, for blizzard belt.

Armstrong Nurseries, Ontario, Calif. Roses, fruit trees, ornamentals.

Bongarzone Nursery, Inc., Wayside Rd., New Shrewsbury, N. J. Trees, shrubs, ground covers.

Buntings' Nurseries, Inc., Selbyville, Del. Fruit and ornamental trees, strawberries.

Garden City Nursery Sales, Inc., Garden City, N. Y. Everbearing strawberries, house plants and accessories.

Gardenside Nurseries, Inc., Shelburne, Vt. Lilies, unusual perennials, general landscaping.

Inter-State Nurseries, Hamburg, Iowa. Roses, trees, shrubs, perennials, bulbs and seeds.

Kansas Landscape and Nursery Co., Salina, Kan. Roses, chrysanthemums.

Kelly Bros. Nurseries, 23 Maple St., Dansville, N. Y. Fruits, dwarf apples, ornamentals, shrubs.

Krider Nurseries, Inc., Middlebury, Ind. Roses, hardy types of trees and plants.

Lehman Gardens, Faribault, Minn. Mums, hybrid clematis, day lilies. Distributors of Dr. Kraus varieties of these.

Lounsberry Gardens, P.O. Box 135, Oakford, Ill. Wildflowers and ferns.

Neosho Nurseries, Neosho, Mo. Evergreens, trees, roses.

Putney Nursery, Inc., Putney, Vt. Wildflowers.

Rayner Bros., Inc., Salisbury, Md. Strawberry and blueberry plants. Distributors of David Hall varieties.

Sarcoxie Nurseries, Wild Bros. Nursery Co., Sarcoxie, Mo. Irises, peonies, day lilies.

Sky Hook Farm, Johnson, Vt. Primroses.

Spring Hill Nurseries Co., Tipp City, Ohio. Miniature roses, fruits, nut trees.

Stern's Nurseries, Inc. 404 Williams St., Geneva, N. Y. Nursery stock, bulbs, berries and fruit trees.

Wayside Gardens Co., Mentor, Ohio. Novelties in shrubs and perennials. Catalogue, $1.

Zilke Bros. Nursery, Baroda, Mich. Select nursery stock, rare and unusual plants and trees.

Landscaping, Shrubs and Trees

Bountiful Ridge Nurseries, Princess Anne, Md. Fruit trees and berry plants.

Brimfield Gardens Nursery, 245 Brimfield Rd., Wethersfield, Conn. Rare trees and shrubs.

Emlong Nurseries, Stevensville, Mich. Fruit plants, dwarf and standard fruit trees.

Earl Ferris Nursery, 60 Bridge St., Hampton, Iowa. Evergreens, shrubs and shade trees.

Louis Gerardi Nursery, Rt. 1, Caseyville, Ill. Northern varieties of grafted nut and persimmon trees.

D. Hill Nursery Co., Rt. 31, Dundee, Ill. World's largest evergreen nursery. Bonsai specialists.

Forrest Keeling Nursery, Elsberry, Mo. Living fence plants, trees.

Henry Leuthardt Nursery, King St., Port Chester, N. Y. Thirty apple varieties, dwarf fruit, espaliered fruit trees.

Mayfair Nurseries, Rt. 2, Nichols, N. Y. Dwarf trees and shrubs.

J. E. Miller Nurseries, W. Lake Rd., Canandaigua, N. Y. All fruits, nut trees.

Stark Bros. Nurseries & Orchards Co. Louisiana, Mo. Fruit trees, dwarf fruit trees, shade trees, shrubs, berries, vines, roses.

Tennessee Nursery Co., P.O. Box 416, Cleveland, Tenn. Standard and dwarf fruit trees.

Woodlot Seed Co., Norway, Mich., Tree and shrub seeds.

Seeds and Supplies

Armchair Explorers, 214 N. Yale, Fullerton, Calif. Rare seeds and books, gesneriads, begonias.

Breck's of Boston, 250 Breck Bldg., Boston 10, Mass. Bulbs, lawn and garden products.

Burgess Seed and Plant Co., Galesburg, Mich. Bulbs, nursery, tomatoes.

W. Atlee Burpee Co., 18th St. & Hunting Park Ave., Philadelphia 32, Pa. Flower, vegetable and lawn grass seed.

Condon Bros. Seedsman, Rockford, Ill. Seeds, bulbs, plants.

De Giorgi Co., Inc., P.O. Box 126, Council Bluffs, Iowa. Vegetable seeds for market gardeners, imported flower seeds.

Farmer Seed and Nursery Co., Dept. FA, Faribault, Minn. Hybrid and miniature vegetables, short season varieties for the North.

Ferry-Morse Seed Co., P.O. Box 778, Detroit, Mich. Packet flower and vegetable seed.

Henry Field and Nursery Co., 407 Sycamor, Shenandoah, Iowa. Garden and field seeds; also nursery stock and house plants.

Joseph Harris Co., Inc., Moreton Farm, Rochester 11, N. Y. Flower and vegetable seeds, garden supplies.

Ivy Hill Forest, Cockeysville, Md. Perkie Plants—Seeds 'n Greetings—attractively packaged. Also nursery stock. Catalogue, 25c.

J. W. Jung Seed Co., Randolph, Wis. Bulbs, shrubs, plants, trees. Extra-early tomato and sweet corn.

Earl May Seed and Nursery Co., Shenandoah, Iowa. Flower and vegetable seeds, nursery stock.

Northrup King and Co., 1500 NE Jackson, Minneapolis, Minn. Wholesale—all seeds from lawn products to farm seeds, flowers.

George W. Park Seed Co., Greenwood, S. C. Flowerseed specialists, 3000 varieties.

Pearce Seed Co., Moorestown, N. J. Unusual seeds, plants and bulbs, perennials.

Plantation gardens, Rustburg, Va. Herb plants and seeds.

R. H. Shumway, Seedsman, 628 Cedar St., Rockford, Ill. Nursery and bulbs, flower and vegetables.

Thompson & Morgan Ltd., Ipswich, England. Rare flower seeds. Has world's most extensive list.

Vaughan's Seed Co., 601 W. Jackson Blvd., Chicago 6, Ill.; 24 Vesey St., New York 7, N. Y. Largest list of flower seeds in U. S. (world's second largest). Specialists in Merion bluegrass. Complete home garden supplies.

Supplies

Flowerwood, Inc., Crystal Lake, Ill. Florists', nursery, garden supplies.

The House Plant Corner, P.O. Box 137, Oxford, Md. African violet supplies and fluorescent light equipment.

Lifetime Markers, 4540 Strathcona Dr., Milford, Mich. Plastic garden markers and tags.

Harvey J. Ridge, 1126 Arthur St., Wausau, Wis. African violet supplies.

O. M. Scott and Sons, Marysville, Ohio. Fertilizers, weed killers, pesticides, spreaders, power mowers.

House Plants

Barrington Greenhouses, Dept. TFA, Barrington, N. J. Unusual indoor plants. Catalogue, 25c.

Havalook Gardens, 10045 Wigrand River, Fowlerville, Mich. Flowershop, herbs. Catalogue, 5c.

Wyndham Hayward Lakemont Gardens, 915 S. Lakemont, Winter Park, Fla. Gingers, caladiums, gesneriads, amaryllids, gloriosa, bromeliaceae.

Cecil Houdyshel Nursery, 1412 Third St., LaVerne, Calif. African violets, bulbs, nursery stock.

House of Plants, 26 Hotchkiss St., South Binghamton, N. Y. Gesneriaceae specialties.

Logee's Greenhouses, 55 North St., Danielson, Conn. Begonias, exotics, geraniums, herbs. Catalogue, 25c.

Julius Roehrs Co., 375 Paterson Ave., Rutherford, N. J. Distributor, house plants. Catalogue, 25c.

Tropical Paradise, 3810 Bales Ave., Kansas City 28, Mo. Rare plants, begonias, ferns, gesneriads. Catalogue, 25c.

Wilson Bros., Roachdale, Ind. Geraniums—fancy-leaved, ivy-leaved, and scented.

Whistling Hill, Box 235, Hamburg, N. Y. Gesneriads, cuttings, seeds, plants.

Yoars Greenhouse, Bunker Hill, Ind. Tropical nursery stock, African violets, foliage plants, begonia.

INDEX

Numbers in boldface type indicate illustrations.

Index • 175

PHOTO CREDITS. FPG, Robert Bagby, p. 160 (bot.); Roy Bales, p. 149 (bot.); Jack Breed, pp. 26 (bot.), 154 (top), 155 (top); George Davis, p. 20; William Eymann, pp. 19 (top, bot. l. & r.), 21 (top), 25 (top r. bot.), 32 (top & bot.), 145 (top), 153 (ctr. & bot.), 154 (bot. l.), 160 (top l.); Phil Fein, p. 148 (top); Paul Genereux, pp. 152 (top & bot. r.). 154 (bot. r.), 155 (bot.); Bud Graybill, p. 146-7; Hampfler Studio, p. 160 (top r.); Rudi Rada, pp. 18 (bot.), 151 (top); Fred H. Ragsdale, pp. 18 (top), 25 (top l.); Julius Shulman, p. 28 (bot.); L. Willinger, p. 26 (top); Philip D. Gendreau, p. 140. Gottscho-Schleisner, pp. 4, 21 (bot.), 22 (top & bot. l.), 23 (top, ctr., & bot.), 24 (top & bot.), 25 (top r. top & bot.), 27 (top & bot.), 28 (top), 29 (ctr., bot.), 30 (top & bot.), 31 (top, bot. l. & r.), 48, 64, 84, 146 (top l., top r., & bot. l.), 147 (top l. & r.), 148 (bot. l. & r.), 149 (top l. & r.), 152 (bot. l.), 153 (top), 156 (top), 157 (top & bot.), 158 (top & bot. l.). Pierre M. Martinot, pp. 22 (bot. ctr. & r.), 145 (bot. l.), 156 (bot. ctr.), 160 (ctr.). Monkmeyer, Jack Roche, pp. 150, 151 (bot.). Courtesy of the Orchid Jungle, Homested, Fla., p. 156 (bot. l.). Photo Researchers, Russ Kinne, pp. 145 (bot. r.), 156 (bot. r.); Julius Fanta, p. 158 (bot. r.); William M. Graham, p. 159 (top r. & bot.). Portland Cement Assoc., p. 29 (top). Courtesy of the Slocum Water Gardens, Binghamton, N. Y., p. 17.
LANDSCAPE & ARCHITECTURAL CREDITS Mary Deputy Catell, Landscape Designer, p. 29 (bot.). Allen F. Dalsimer, Landscape Designer, pp. 23 (ctr.), 24 (top), 30 (top). M. K. & E. H. Hunter, Architects, p. 150 (bot. l.). Innocenti & Webel, Landscape Architects, pp. 22 (top), 29 (ctr.), 156 (top). Designed by Mrs. H. I. Nicholas, p. 30 (top). Alfred Shaknis, Architect, p. 23 (top). Clayton Steen, Architect (Home of Mr. & Mrs. Devon Francis, White Plains, N. Y.), p. 28 (top). Frede Stege, Landscape Architect, p. 31 (top).